CONTENTS

D1312518

On the Cover

Transportation of the future will feature electric vehicles, charging infrastructure, electric air taxis, and hydrogen-powered airliners that emit mostly water vapor and heat.

ILLUSTRATION: BOSE COLLINS

ABOVE: A mural in the
St. Albans area of Queens,
New York, honors some of
the Black luminaries who've
lived there, including Ella
Fitzgerald and Lena Horne.

THE FUTURE
IS ELECTRIC

Planes (and Trains) and Automobiles

BY **SUSAN GOLDBERG**   PHOTOGRAPH BY **DAVIDE MONTELEONE**

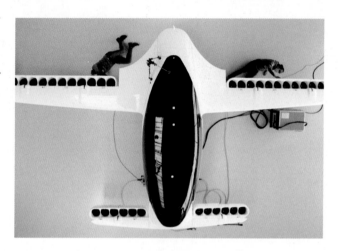

WE'RE IN THE MIDDLE of one revolution—and are soon to launch another. These upheavals, both leading to a more sustainable future, are the products not of human conflict but of human ingenuity. Simply put, we're utterly reinventing how we get from here to there.

"Cars and trucks are undergoing their greatest makeover since the automobile's inception more than a century ago," writer Craig Welch notes in the first of this issue's two stories on the future of transportation. Almost overnight, electric cars are proliferating, as carbon dioxide-belching internal combustion engines head for the endangered species list.

In air transportation, the other mode we examine, change is more gradual. There are promising developments in sustainable aviation fuel made from waste products, planes fueled by "green" hydrogen, and aircraft with zero-emission, battery-powered electric engines.

Most market-level change still is on the horizon. For example, says writer Sam Howe Verhovek, there's no battery that can get a Boeing 747 from New York to London: "It would take the juice of 4.4 million laptop batteries just to generate liftoff. Except that the jumbo jet could never get off the ground: The batteries would weigh seven times as much as the plane."

Concern about climate change is driving these economic and consumer shifts. But progress is taking too long: Our planet's health depends on zeroing out carbon dioxide emissions by 2050 at the latest, climate change experts say.

That's a sobering truth, but there's reason for optimism in this issue's coverage of what we're achieving now (with autos) and what we're poised to achieve (with planes). Global annual sales of electric vehicles are expected to soar from just over three million today to 14 million by 2025. By 2040, EVs likely will make up 70 percent of cars globally. As for planes, Verhovek says, "George Jetson's flying car is indeed on the way, albeit with AI and not George at the controls." We depict the plane of the future in a graphic on pages 74-5. It looks like a flying boomerang with passenger seats in the wings.

As we planned this issue, I imagined using the headline "Planes, Trains, and Automobiles," after the 1987 comedy film that's nominally about transportation but mostly about the indomitable human spirit. However, as scrupulous editors noted, that would not meet our accuracy standards unless we mentioned rail transport in our coverage.

So, we shall. In the United States, railway electrification is practically nil. But in Europe, China, and India, trains are more than 55 percent electrified, and India's aiming for nearly 100 percent by 2024. Though rail accounts for just one percent of transport emissions globally, every bit helps.

Thank you for reading *National Geographic*. □

Engineers, seen from overhead, work on a five-seat prototype of an air taxi in Munich. Built by German aerospace company Lilium, this model demonstrated on its first flight, in 2019, that electric fan power can propel vertical takeoff and landing as well as horizontal flight. The company is scaling up the same technology for a seven-seater that will fly at a top speed of 175 mph with a flight range of at least 155 miles.

Chief financial officer. Caregiver. Eclipse chaser.
A life well planned allows you to

LIVE *YOUR* LIFE.
—

While you may not be closing a business deal and taking your mother and daughter on a once-in-a-lifetime adventure — your life is just as unique. Backed by sophisticated resources and a team of specialists in every field, a Raymond James financial advisor can help you plan for the dreams you have, the way you care for those you love and how you choose to give back. So you can live *your* life.

RAYMOND JAMES
LIFE WELL PLANNED.

PROOF

NATIONAL GEOGRAPHIC
VOL. 240 NO. 4

POISONED BEAUTY

PHOTOGRAPHS BY
GHEORGHE POPA

In images that could be mistaken for paintings, a photographer records how mine waste has ruined a valley near his Romanian hometown.

LOOKING
AT THE
EARTH
FROM
EVERY
POSSIBLE
ANGLE

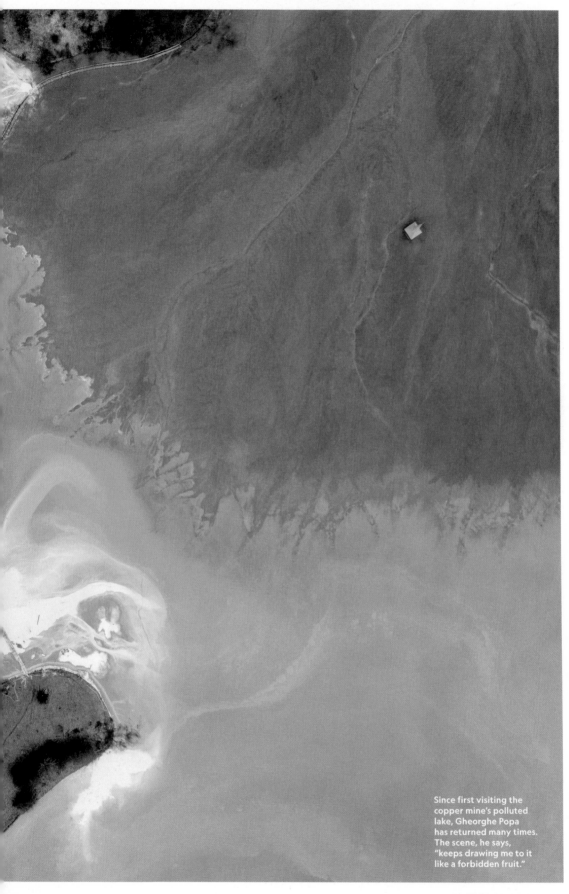

Since first visiting the copper mine's polluted lake, Gheorghe Popa has returned many times. The scene, he says, "keeps drawing me to it like a forbidden fruit."

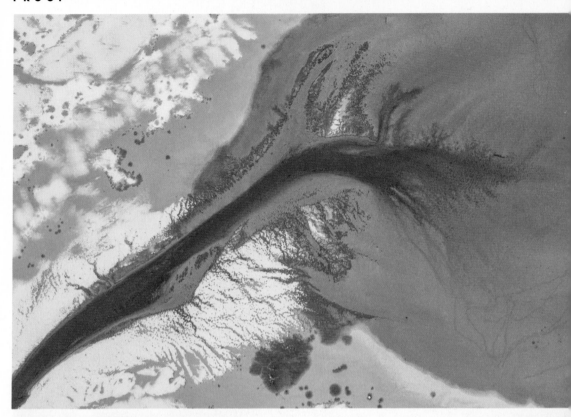

Waste from the Roșia Poieni mine is filling the Șesii Valley, in western Romania, with a colorful brew. The watery mix includes tailings—material left after the separation of valuable raw ore—which can be hazardous if not properly contained.

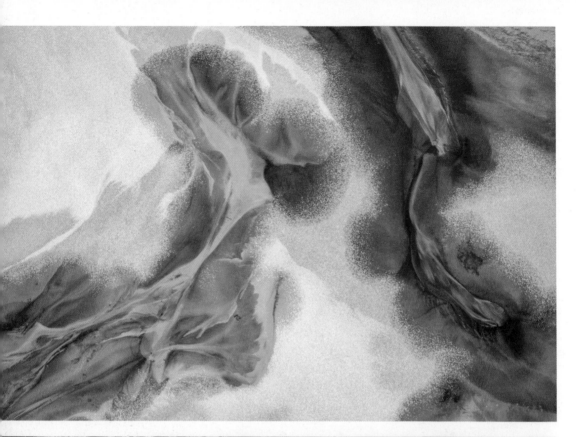

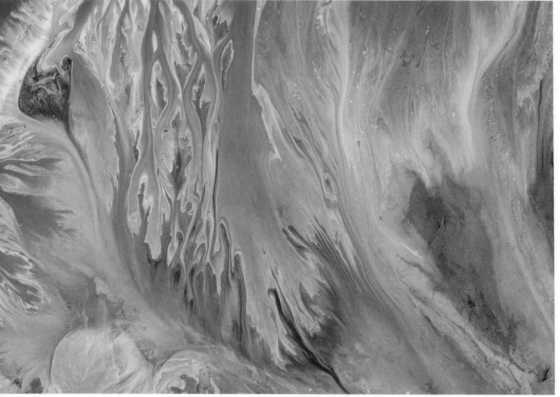

Popa sees a duality in his drone photographs of the contaminated site: The lake's bright colors, he writes, are both "surreally beautiful" and "repulsive by their nature."

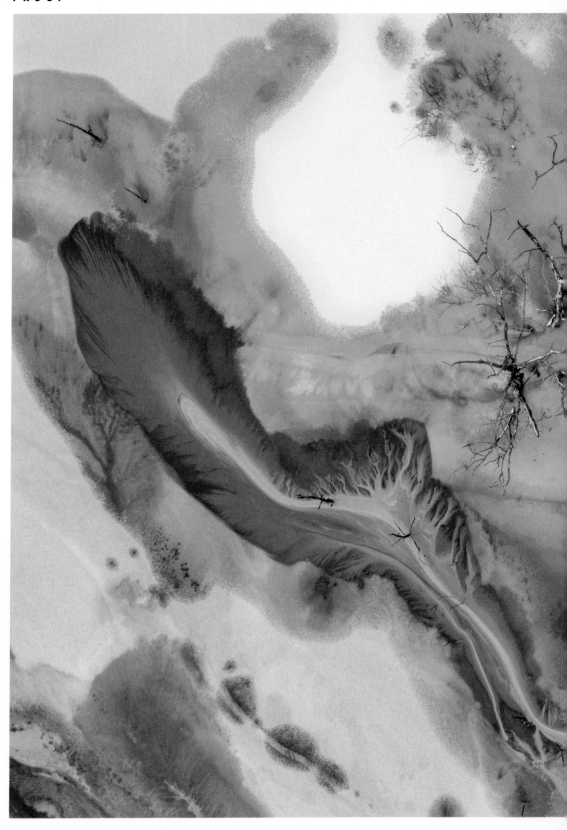

For some 20 years after mining began in the late 1970s, the Romanian government evacuated hundreds of residents of the village of Geamăna. Villagers say that officials promised to relocate their cemetery but never did.

Buildings in Geamăna were also left in place. Each year, the water level rises by roughly three feet, swallowing more of the village. Houses, roads, trees: All are sinking beneath the slurry.

THE BACKSTORY

A PHOTOGRAPHER MOUNTS AN ARTISTIC PROTEST AGAINST INDUSTRIAL POLLUTION IN IDYLLIC TRANSYLVANIA.

THE ROȘIA POIENI copper mine appears like a wound on Romania's Apuseni Mountains. An open-pit mine operated by a state-owned company, it draws from the largest copper deposit in the country. In 1978, needing somewhere to discard the mine's waste, President Nicolae Ceaușescu initiated the removal of residents from the neighboring village of Geamăna. Water and the mine's sludge were then released into the village and the Șesii Valley, forming an artificial, partly viscous lake.

Gheorghe Popa grew up about two hours away by car, in the town of Aiud, at the base of the Apuseni Mountains. A pharmacist and nature photographer, Popa first encountered the dumping site in 2014. "To this day," he wrote in the Romanian edition of *National Geographic,* "I can't forget that chemical smell that even filled my mouth." The unearthly scene mesmerized him: amid an otherwise picturesque mountain range, a lake tie-dyed in swirls of yellow, red, orange, and turquoise.

During subsequent visits, Popa deployed a drone to capture bird's-eye views. The polluted valley has been fertile ground for his work: The visage of the lake and the possibilities for photographing it are always changing, depending on the substances poured into it, the time of year or day, and the quality of the light.

A small number of residents remain near the lake, hanging on in homes above the rising waterline. Some living in the area work at the mine. Popa also has witnessed ducks gliding across the lake's multicolored surface. He hopes his photographs—though they may be inviting at first glance—will prove cautionary to viewers. In his words, "I wish the 'beauty' of this disaster could forever remind us that we must never let something like this happen again."

—HICKS WOGAN

One day it may disappear, but for now the spire of Geamăna's early 19th-century church remains visible, poking out of the lake at the center of this image.

HAVE YOU ROLLED OVER?

| CHANGE THE WORLD WITH YOUR IRA ROLLOVER

If you are at least 70 ½ years old, you can transfer up to $100,000 directly to the National Geographic Society from a traditional IRA without paying income tax on the withdrawal—and help you meet your required minimum distribution. Your gift will help us make a lasting impact in the fields of science, exploration, education, and storytelling.

To discuss your IRA charitable rollover, simply notify your IRA administrator or access our free estate planning tool at www.givingdocs.com/national-geographic/

Contact us for further information toll free at (800) 226-4438 or email us at legacy@ngs.org

NATIONAL GEOGRAPHIC

EXPLORE

IN THIS SECTION
A New Ocean Map
Angelina, Bee Advocate
Murmurations 101
Frozen Into the Arctic

ILLUMINATING THE MYSTERIES—AND WONDERS—ALL AROUND US EVERY DAY

NATIONAL GEOGRAPHIC | VOL. 240 NO. 4

The Persistence of Pay Inequity

FOR EACH DOLLAR A MAN IS PAID IN THE U.S., A WOMAN IS PAID LESS, SOMETIMES HALF AS MUCH. WHY HAVEN'T WE CLOSED THE GAP?

BY **HELENA MARÍA VIRAMONTES**

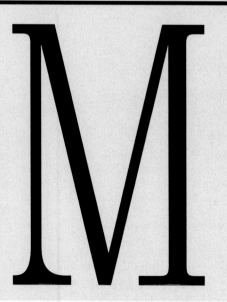

M

MY MOTHER UPHELD a steely work ethic. Laboring in the fields, and laboring through 11 live births—news that made our local East Los Angeles newspaper—how could she not? She had grown up in L.A. during the violent anti-Mexican deportation raids of the 1920s and '30s, when massive sweeps herded immigrants and citizens alike. And although she believed in marriage, she became bitterly resentful of her financial dependence on my father. Thus she was determined to prevent her six daughters, us girls, from falling into the same predicaments. With the capricious raids always reminding her how "disposable" we were as Latinas, she strove to create a female tribe unafraid of hard work, a loving commune unto ourselves.

At home, there was no expectation of charity. We worked for every need outside of the shelter and food provided by our American-born parents; we had jobs even while going to school, fueled by an

FOR EACH $1 A MAN MAKES ...

... **A WOMAN MAKES 82 CENTS** (among full-time, year-round U.S. workers). That gender wage gap varies notably by state, and it is dramatically wider for most women of color. It's so wide, in fact, that October 21 is Equal Pay Day for Latinas because they need that long—one whole year plus 10 months of a second—to make what non-Hispanic white men make in a single year. The COVID-19 pandemic pushed more women than men out of their jobs; that likely will exacerbate the wage gap in the long run as women return to the workforce.

BY **MONICA SERRANO, IRENE BERMAN-VAPORIS, AND KELSEY NOWAKOWSKI**

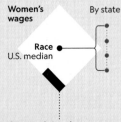

Diamond size shows wage losses over a lifetime, based on today's wage gap.

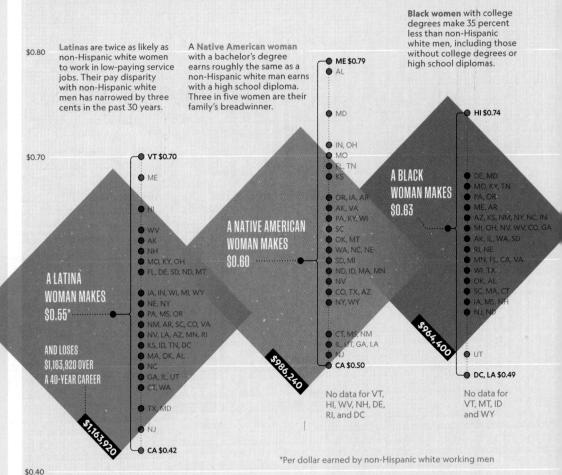

Black women with college degrees make 35 percent less than non-Hispanic white men, including those without college degrees or high school diplomas.

Latinas are twice as likely as non-Hispanic white women to work in low-paying service jobs. Their pay disparity with non-Hispanic white men has narrowed by three cents in the past 30 years.

A **Native American woman** with a bachelor's degree earns roughly the same as a non-Hispanic white man earns with a high school diploma. Three in five women are their family's breadwinner.

A LATINA WOMAN MAKES $0.55*

AND LOSES $1,163,920 OVER A 40-YEAR CAREER

$1,163,920

A NATIVE AMERICAN WOMAN MAKES $0.60

$986,240

A BLACK WOMAN MAKES $0.63

$964,400

$0.80

$0.70

$0.40

Latina column:
VT $0.70
ME
HI
WV
AK
NH
MO, KY, OH
FL, DE, SD, ND, MT
IA, IN, WI, MI, WY
NE, NY
PA, MS, OR
NM, AR, SC, CO, VA
NV, LA, AZ, MN, RI
KS, ID, TN, DC
MA, OK, AL
NC
GA, IL, UT
CT, WA
TX, MD
NJ
CA $0.42

Native American column:
ME $0.79
AL
MD
IN, OH
MO
FL, TN
KS
OR, IA, AR
AK, VA
PA, KY, WI
SC
OK, MT
WA, NC, NE
SD, MI
ND, ID, MA, MN
NV
CO, TX, AZ
NY, WY
CT, MS, NM
IL, UT, GA, LA
NJ
CA $0.50

No data for VT, HI, WV, NH, DE, RI, and DC

Black column:
HI $0.74
DE, MD
MO, KY, TN
PA, OR
ME, AR
AZ, KS, NM, NY, NC, IN
MI, OH, NV, WV, CO, GA
AK, IL, WA, SD
RI, NE
MN, FL, CA, VA
WI, TX
OK, AL
SC, MA, CT
IA, MS, NH
NJ, ND
UT
DC, LA $0.49

No data for VT, MT, ID and WY

*Per dollar earned by non-Hispanic white working men

unshakable resolve for a better future. Only later did it occur to me that our labor was defined by our gendered, working-class brown bodies, whether in the arduous responsibility of keeping a large household functioning or the backbreaking tyrannies of the California fields where we picked grapes in the summer. Our labor was measured in units of sweat and muscle, visceral, visible evidence of what my mother understood as honest work.

My years in college introduced me to another mode of labor, one that manifested in the sacred privilege Toni Morrison once called being in companionship with your own mind. That's when I began to understand how some kinds of work—and some kinds of workers—were perceived as less than others. It was my good fortune to attend a college established by an order of Roman Catholic nuns who were feminists, activist teachers, and staunch humanitarians. Many of them chose to renounce their vows and form a nonprofit lay community rather than follow the

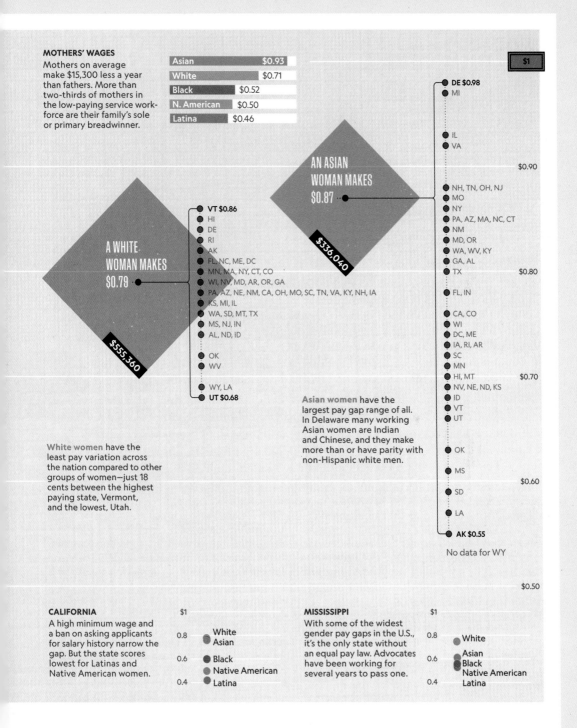

MOTHERS' WAGES

Mothers on average make $15,300 less a year than fathers. More than two-thirds of mothers in the low-paying service workforce are their family's sole or primary breadwinner.

Asian	$0.93
White	$0.71
Black	$0.52
N. American	$0.50
Latina	$0.46

$1

AN ASIAN WOMAN MAKES $0.87

$336,040

A WHITE WOMAN MAKES $0.79

$555,360

White women column:
- VT $0.86
- HI
- DE
- RI
- AK
- FL, NC, ME, DC
- MN, MA, NY, CT, CO
- WI, NV, MD, AR, OR, GA
- PA, AZ, NE, NM, CA, OH, MO, SC, TN, VA, KY, NH, IA
- KS, MI, IL
- WA, SD, MT, TX
- MS, NJ, IN
- AL, ND, ID
- OK
- WV
- WY, LA
- UT $0.68

Asian women column:
- DE $0.98
- MI
- IL
- VA
- $0.90
- NH, TN, OH, NJ
- MO
- NY
- PA, AZ, MA, NC, CT
- NM
- MD, OR
- WA, WV, KY
- GA, AL
- TX — $0.80
- FL, IN
- CA, CO
- WI
- DC, ME
- IA, RI, AR
- SC
- MN
- HI, MT — $0.70
- NV, NE, ND, KS
- ID
- VT
- UT
- OK
- MS
- $0.60
- SD
- LA
- AK $0.55

No data for WY

$0.50

White women have the least pay variation across the nation compared to other groups of women—just 18 cents between the highest paying state, Vermont, and the lowest, Utah.

Asian women have the largest pay gap range of all. In Delaware many working Asian women are Indian and Chinese, and they make more than or have parity with non-Hispanic white men.

CALIFORNIA

A high minimum wage and a ban on asking applicants for salary history narrow the gap. But the state scores lowest for Latinas and Native American women.

$1
0.8 — White / Asian
0.6 — Black / Native American
0.4 — Latina

MISSISSIPPI

With some of the widest gender pay gaps in the U.S., it's the only state without an equal pay law. Advocates have been working for several years to pass one.

$1
0.8 — White
0.6 — Asian / Black / Native American
0.4 — Latina

---

strict dictates of the patriarchal cardinal archbishop of Los Angeles. Their fearless actions widened my understandings of oppression and loving resistance.

I received a college diploma, the first woman in our family to do so, and returned home to seek honest work that would be deserving of equitable pay. After months of dismal interview failures—I was not skilled in clerical work, cashier work, or nursing, jobs held by my older sisters—and before I secured an unlikely position bottling beer on a Pabst brewery assembly line, I had enrolled in a creative writing class at Cal State L.A.

Every time I opened my spiral notebook at our dining table to journal an assignment or write a poem, it disturbed my mother. I was unemployed, and it bothered her to see me sitting and staring into space. She would ask me to go water the peach tree or sweep the porches or wash the dinner dishes in the sink, chores that could surely have waited at the very least another half hour. It wasn't until one

WAGE GAP DATA IS LACKING IN SOME STATES DUE TO INSUFFICIENT POPULATION SAMPLE SIZES.
SOURCE: JASMINE TUCKER, NATIONAL WOMEN'S LAW CENTER

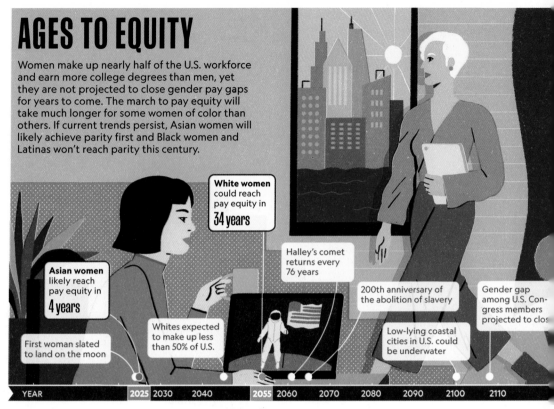

AGES TO EQUITY

Women make up nearly half of the U.S. workforce and earn more college degrees than men, yet they are not projected to close gender pay gaps for years to come. The march to pay equity will take much longer for some women of color than others. If current trends persist, Asian women will likely achieve parity first and Black women and Latinas won't reach parity this century.

White women could reach pay equity in **34 years**

Asian women likely reach pay equity in **4 years**

Halley's comet returns every 76 years

200th anniversary of the abolition of slavery

Gender gap among U.S. Congress members projected to clos

First woman slated to land on the moon

Whites expected to make up less than 50% of U.S.

Low-lying coastal cities in U.S. could be underwater

YEAR   2025 2030   2040   2055 2060   2070   2080   2090   2100   2110

PROJECTIONS BASED ON PACE OF CHANGE FOR THE PAST 50 YEARS. DATA FOR NATIVE AMERICANS NOT AVAILABLE. GENERATION DEFINED AS A 25-YEAR PERIOD.

of my short stories won first prize in a university literary contest, a whopping $25, that the labor paradigm shifted. When my mother approached me with another housekeeping duty, I handed her the check. "Where did you get this?" she asked, because to us in 1976, this amount might as well have been $250. "I got it for my writing," I replied. She slipped the check in her apron pocket and left the room, returning with a cup of coffee for me.

That check helped my mother believe my talent could enable me to earn a living and take care of myself, and her confidence helped me aspire to a writing career yet to be imagined. My sisters, in turn, gave me something else: a sense of self-worth, as it would be my job to tell their stories. All I had to do was get past our country's walls—persistent prejudicial walls, literal and figurative border walls constructed to keep me from fully realizing my value. I realized then that I couldn't *not* write.

I write because I want us to think about where we place value, and how systemic gender and racial discrimination promotes a devaluation of people and their labor. There is evidence of that in the pay gap data. Even when analysts control for factors that are known to influence pay—such as race, industry, education, and work experience—they can't explain what causes more than one-third of the gap between men's and women's pay. But how else to interpret the unexplained portion of the gender pay gap other than discrimination?

U.S. history is rooted in colonization, genocide of Indigenous peoples, and chattel slavery, which have always maintained the subordination of women (here I include cis, trans, genderfluid—all women). Without bravely coming to terms with our history's residue of violent discrimination, we will never fully understand pay gaps and the persistence of this shameful inequality.

ALTHOUGH WOMEN'S LABOR was crucial in both the private sphere of home and public sphere of community, during the industrial revolution it became devalued because it did not produce satisfactory profit, according to anti-racist feminist activist Angela Davis. Treating women's work as inferior kept it cheap and gave rise to a systemic erosion of respect that justified pay inequity based on gender, race, or both.

Law and sociology professor Dorothy Roberts explains how the separation of women's housework into two grades, the spiritual and the menial, creates a racialized hierarchy of women's labor. Supervision of the household and guiding children in their moral education is the spiritual work that came to be the province of privileged white women. The taxing and tedious menial housework—less valued because it is deemed to require less skill and intellect—is

200th anniversary of woman suffrage in U.S.

Gender gap in computer science research workforce projected to close

Black women could reach pay equity in

112 years, or 4.5 generations

Halley's comet is back

400th anniversary of United States' independence

Latinas projected to reach pay equity in

199 years, or 8 generations

Pluto is closer to the sun than Neptune, which occurs every 248 years

Halley's comet is back again

2120 2133 2140 2150 2160 2170 2180 2190 2200 2210 2220 2230

MONICA SERRANO, NGM STAFF. KELSEY NOWAKOWSKI, IRENE BERMAN-VAPORIS. ILLUSTRATION: GERALDINE SY
SOURCES: INSTITUTE FOR WOMEN'S POLICY RESEARCH; NASA; U.S. CENSUS; NOAA

associated with immigrants and women of color. To this day, data show that "menial" workers continue to be disproportionately women of color.

As a Chicana writer, I needed to understand how discriminatory practices worked so that I could tear them down one word at a time, erase the stereotypes about us. It was an act of love between my mother and me; in accepting her cup of coffee, I made a soulful commitment to make our struggles fully visible.

Often working in the shadows of communities, Latinas accept low wages and the least desirable jobs. Most receive no health insurance, no sick or vacation time off, and certainly no childcare.

The National Farm Worker Ministry considers women farmworkers "arguably the most exploited workers in this country, even more vulnerable than male farmworkers." So in my first novel, *Under the Feet of Jesus,* I wrote about the lives of Latina farmworkers, my *hermanas* everywhere—I never forgot their plight because I had been one of them.

Given their varying degrees of citizenship—a large number undocumented—there is little recourse for Latina farmworkers who are mistreated and fear losing their jobs. They endure the grueling circumstances of picking, planting, pruning, heat stress, and exposure to pesticides, as well as what Dolores Huerta, co-founding member of the United Farm Workers, has called "an epidemic" of sexual assault and harassment.

Farm-working Latinas are building collectives like Alianza Nacional de Campesinas, which advocates for immigration reform and human rights. But their fight for wage equality will be won only if Me Too, Black Lives Matter, and LGBTQ movements are also successful in fostering racial and gender equality. First on the agenda: a reminder that these workers are not expendable but an essential component of our everyday existence. The beans for our morning coffee and the vegetables for our dinner were most likely harvested by a farm-working Latina. They help feed a nation and a world. Even through a pandemic.

When my children were young, I hung a poster in our house that announced, "Women Hold Up Half the Sky." It's a poetic image meant to inspire, but sometimes I reflect on the weight of the world and how that strenuous task is exhausting for working-class Latinas like my mother, my sisters, all of us in my community. The image implies a necessary defiance against the rules of gravity, a battle we fight every minute against the insufficient paychecks that seek to mark us as somehow less than human.

Farm-working Latinas are owed pathways to citizenship—and, with all women, fair pay and recognition. Haven't we worked hard enough? □

Helena María Viramontes is the author, most recently, of *Their Dogs Came With Them,* a novel. She is Distinguished Professor of Arts and Sciences in English at Cornell University.

Driven to capture the night sky

National Geographic photographer Babak Tafreshi and top NASCAR driver Bubba Wallace team up to capture the stars.

WRITTEN BY **SUSAN DAUGHERTY**

What could pointing a race car toward the finish line and pointing a camera at the Milky Way have in common? More than you might imagine.

Race car driver Bubba Wallace is famed for his social justice work, along with being the first African American in 50 years to win in one of NASCAR's top three national touring series. Babak Tafreshi is a renowned National Geographic photographer and master of night sky imagery. Together they journeyed to Utah's remote Gooseberry Mesa for a National Geographic adventure aimed at taking Bubba's passion for photography to the next level.

For decades, Babak has spent nights under the stars on all seven continents, using nightscape

photography to bridge art and science. Bubba finds photography a perfect counterbalance to the roaring intensity of competition on the track. "It's a peaceful escape that lets me slow down and enjoy the moment. The destinations I want to explore are all inspired by photography. But I'm a rookie, so learning from a pro like Babak was an exciting chance to expand my horizons."

Gooseberry Mesa is far from population centers in a designated area protected from nighttime light pollution—a paradise for astral photographers. Natural night environments such as this are rare. Two-thirds of the world's population lives where the Milky Way is no longer visible, a fact that fuels Babak's efforts to document and protect the night sky as a natural resource for future generations.

Camping, hiking, and shooting in the mesa's rough terrain brought parallels between photography and racing into focus. Bubba notes, "You strap in, go through your checks, and once you fire up the engine there's no turning back—I know I'll be in that seat for more than three hours." Babak agrees, "I have the same feeling as soon as I touch the wheel of my camera and change the exposure—I'm ready to continue through the entire night." For Bubba, developing patience allowed him to mature as a driver and is equally essential to his photography. "With time-lapse, I may spend hours capturing 1,500 frames just for a couple of seconds of film. It can be frustrating until you accept that you can't rush things."

Seizing the moment is crucial too. "Every minute things are changing," Babak explains. "The Earth's shadow, the moonlight, the rise of constellations, a meteor—if you lose the moment, it's gone forever." Bubba likens the physical and mental demands of racing to his nights tackling Utah's rugged landscape, high elevations, and subfreezing temperatures. "Out there and on the track, it takes endurance to stay focused the entire time." Preparation is also key. "I want to advance beyond turning on the camera and shooting automatically. Just like I know the ins and outs of a race car, I need to deepen my understanding of the night sky and the camera—exposure levels, composition, the balance of foreground and background, and fundamental astronomy. At the track you're fighting for thousands of an inch; with a camera it's fractions of exposures. In both cases, going for that edge to be perfect takes total commitment."

Think incoming clouds, wind, or mist will ruin your chance at a perfect shot? According to Babak, "With wide-angle nightscapes every unexpected weather condition can be an opportunity. Our photos show oranges and blues in the corona around the moon you wouldn't see under a clear sky."

As the sun sets in the desert, temperatures dive. Fast. The team was outfitted with Columbia gear to face the subfreezing conditions. For Babak, Columbia passed the test by keeping him warm without getting in the way of executing his craft.

PHOTOGRAPHY BY BUBBA WALLACE

For Bubba, "Gear should help you do more of what you love—and it did."

The team discovered shared interests that transcend photography. "We're both passionate about bringing cultures together and using our work to break down boundaries," says Babak. "The night sky has a unifying power. The new moon that appears over the Southwest United States was seen a few hours earlier in Europe. Even earlier, that moon was hanging over a mosque in the Middle East. Before that, people in a Buddhist temple in Nepal had the same view. The sky connects the whole world under one umbrella."

"I'm excited to keep shooting with the new confidence and skills I've gained," shares Bubba. "I have so many ideas I want to test. They say you miss 100 percent of the shots you don't take. That applies to many things in life, but especially photography."

" It's a peaceful escape that lets me slow down and enjoy the moment. "

BUBBA WALLACE

THE FRIGID FIFTH OCEAN OF THE SOUTH

NEWLY RECOGNIZED BY NATIONAL GEOGRAPHIC, the Southern Ocean joins the Arctic, Atlantic, Indian, and Pacific as a primary division of Earth's marine environment. For our maps, the northern limit has been set at 60° south latitude (with adjustments for the Scotia Sea and Drake Passage), a compromise given the shifting path of the west-to-east–flowing Antarctic Circumpolar Current ringing Antarctica. Scientists consider these waters—colder and denser but less salty—a separate ocean, bounded by the strong current.

BY **MATTHEW W. CHWASTYK**

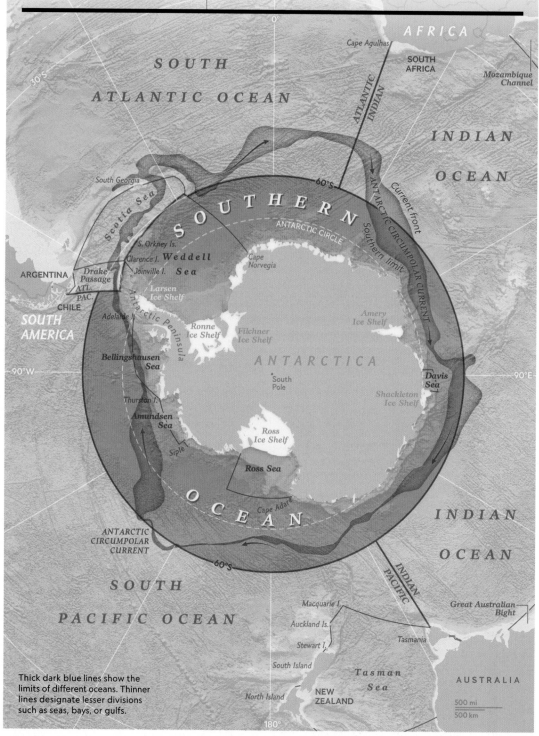

Thick dark blue lines show the limits of different oceans. Thinner lines designate lesser divisions such as seas, bays, or gulfs.

SOURCES: AUSTRALIAN ANTARCTIC DATA CENTER; INTERNATIONAL HYDROGRAPHIC ORGANIZATION; NASA

48%

OF DOMESTIC VIOLENCE VICTIMS DON'T LEAVE BECAUSE THEY CAN'T BRING THEIR PETS

We're changing that.

Through the Purple Leash Project, Purina and RedRover are raising awareness of this critical issue and are working to create more pet-friendly domestic violence shelters in every state. To see how you can help people and pets stay together and heal together, visit **PurpleLeashProject.com.**

Purina trademarks are owned by Société des Produits Nestlé S.A.
Any other marks are property of their respective owners.

PURINA Your Pet, Our Passion.

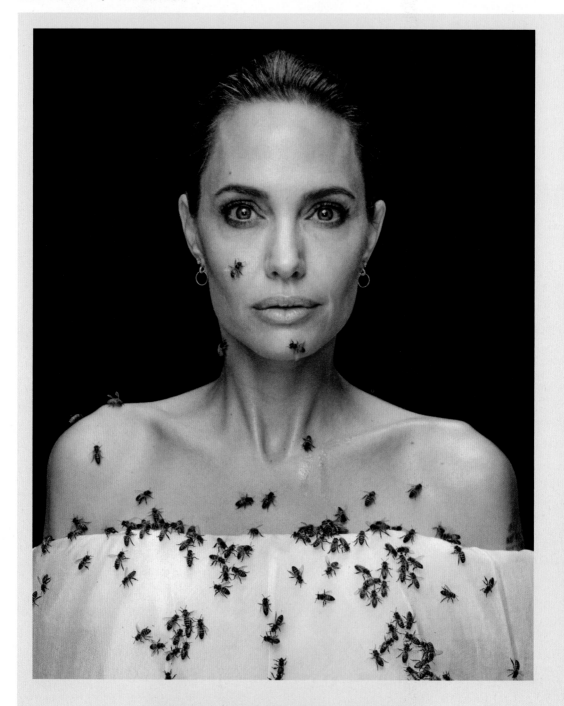

GENERATING BUZZ

—

ANGELINA JOLIE TALKS ABOUT HER LOVE OF BEES, TRAINING WOMEN
TO CARE FOR THEM, AND POSING FOR THIS STRIKING IMAGE.

INTERVIEW BY **INDIRA LAKSHMANAN**
PHOTOGRAPH BY **DAN WINTERS**

IT'S STARTLING at first glance to see an iconic beauty swarmed by bees. A closer look tells a deeper story of the delicate balance between humans and the insects that pollinate much of our food. Angelina Jolie wanted to draw attention to the need to protect bees and to Women for Bees, a UNESCO-Guerlain program training women as beekeepers in 25 biospheres from Ethiopia to China. Photographer Dan Winters, an amateur beekeeper, drew inspiration from a 1981 Richard Avedon portrait of a beekeeper whose naked torso was covered in bees. Jolie was inspired by different visions: bees as indispensable pillars of our food supply, under threat from parasites, pesticides, habitat loss, and climate change—and the global network of women who will protect them.

Three out of four leading food crops depend in part on pollinators, but honeybee populations have suffered mass die-offs in the past 15 years. Jolie sees links among a healthy environment, food security, and women's empowerment. "With so much we are worried about around the world and so many people feeling overwhelmed with bad news," she envisions tangible solutions to this challenge. "This is one that we can manage."

You've been a champion for 20 years now for vulnerable populations, especially women and children. What's the link between at-risk people and threats to bees?
A lot of the at-risk people are displaced because of climate change, or wars that may have sparked from a fight over dwindling resources. Having your environment destroyed, your livelihood stripped from you, is one of the many reasons that people migrate or are displaced or fight. This is all interconnected.

Pollinators, of course, are extremely vital to our life and our environment. And so we have to understand scientifically what happens if we lose them.

What's exciting to me is that instead of stepping forward and saying, "We are losing the bees, we have certain species that have gone extinct, are going extinct," we're coming forward to say, "Yes, this is how you have to protect." You have to be more conscious of chemicals and deforestation. What's exciting is that we're coming at this with solutions [and] empowering women in their livelihoods.

There are some simple ways every one of us can help: planting native vegetation, not using harmful chemicals in our own yards and community gardens.
I don't think a lot of people know what damage they're doing. A lot of people are just trying to get through their day. They want to do good. They don't want to be destructive. They don't know

which thing to buy. They don't know which thing to use. So I think part of this is wanting to help it be simple for everybody, because I need that. I have six kids and a lot happening, and I don't know how to be the perfect anything. And so if we can help each other to say, "This is a way forward, simple, and this is something you can do with your kids."

Have your own children inspired your interest in conservation and the environment?
They're certainly growing up much more informed. Listen, it's down to their generation. We're at the wire. Decisions made and things that we do in the next 10, 20 years are going to make or break the way we're able to live on this planet. Sadly, they know that. That's very hard for them. I can't imagine being a little kid again. Whether the Earth will be able to exist in the same way, and whether there will be bees and pollination, was not something I was thinking about at 12 years old.

Honeybees practice a form of democracy in which individual bees vote on choosing a new nest location. It feels like a nice parallel to Women for Bees. Why involve women in beekeeping, and how will it give them voice, leadership, economic clout?
Women are so capable. And there are many women in areas that have not had opportunities. But they are hungry to learn; they have great business instincts. To have a network, learning how to be the best beekeepers with all the latest science and methods, and having something they can make and sell.

When a woman learns a skill, she teaches other women and other men and her children. And so if you really want something done and you want it magnified, you find a woman and you help her understand what the problem is, and she will work very hard to make sure everyone in the community knows.

For this extraordinary portrait, you were literally covered with bees, and they were flying in front of your face. What did it feel like?
I'm going to sound like my Buddhist practices, but it just felt lovely to be connected to these beautiful creatures. There's certainly a hum. You have to be really still and in your body, in the moment, which is not easy for me. I think part of the thought behind it was, this creature is seen as dangerous sometimes or stinging. So how do we just be with it? The intention is we share this planet. We are affected by each other. This is what it should feel like and it really did, and I felt very honored and very lucky to have the experience.

I did have one that got under my dress the entire time. It was like one of those old comedies. I kept feeling it on my knee, on my leg, and then I thought, Oh, this is the worst place to get stung—it's getting really close. It stayed there the entire time we were doing the shoot. And then when I got all the other bees off, I lifted the skirt, and she went away. □

THIS INTERVIEW HAS BEEN EDITED FOR LENGTH AND CLARITY.

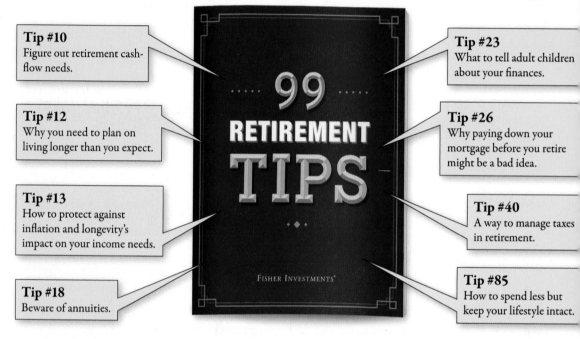

Grind glass, get sand
Sand is chosen to make everything from glass to chemicals, and the high demand for it has left some beaches lacking. One company, Export, has created machines that do the reverse, turning glass bottles into fine grains that can be used in place of real sand by a variety of industries. —AR

DISPATCHES FROM THE FRONT LINES OF SCIENCE AND INNOVATION

GENETICS

A fly that's a gene thief

Many plants protect themselves by producing toxins that act as natural pesticides. But the strategy doesn't work on whiteflies (*Bemisia tabaci*), because some 35 million years ago, they acquired a gene that neutralizes such toxins. The flies got this gene, scientists in China have discovered, by "stealing" it from a plant, probably when a fly ate a plant infected with a virus. This is one of the first known cases of functional gene transfer between plants and animals. —AR

BIOMETRICS

WHO'S THAT BEAR?

A NEW HIGH-TECH TOOL PROMISES TO HELP SCIENTISTS IDENTIFY AND PROTECT GRIZZLIES.

FACIAL-RECOGNITION SYSTEMS for humans are widely used by security services and law enforcement. Now there's one for grizzly bears. The so-called BearID could enable researchers to track the animals across vast stretches of time and space. Identifying individual grizzlies has long been difficult because they tend to lack clearly distinguishable markings. This technology, born of a collaboration between ecologists and computer scientists, makes it possible to easily recognize bears caught by camera traps. With an accuracy rate of 83.9 percent, the software runs deep-learning algorithms to detect and map each grizzly's facial features so the bears can be identified. Indigenous communities in British Columbia are already putting the application to work, monitoring specific bears across territorial boundaries. The developers of BearID hope to adapt their software to track other species too, such as woodland caribou and polar bears. Doing so, they say, will help scientists gain insight into the lives of these animals and aid in their conservation. —ANNIE ROTH

PHOTOS: MELANIE CLAPHAM, UNIVERSITY OF VICTORIA, BRITISH COLUMBIA (BEARS); REBECCA HALE, NGM STAFF (BOTTLE); CSIRO/WIKIMEDIA COMMONS (FLIES)

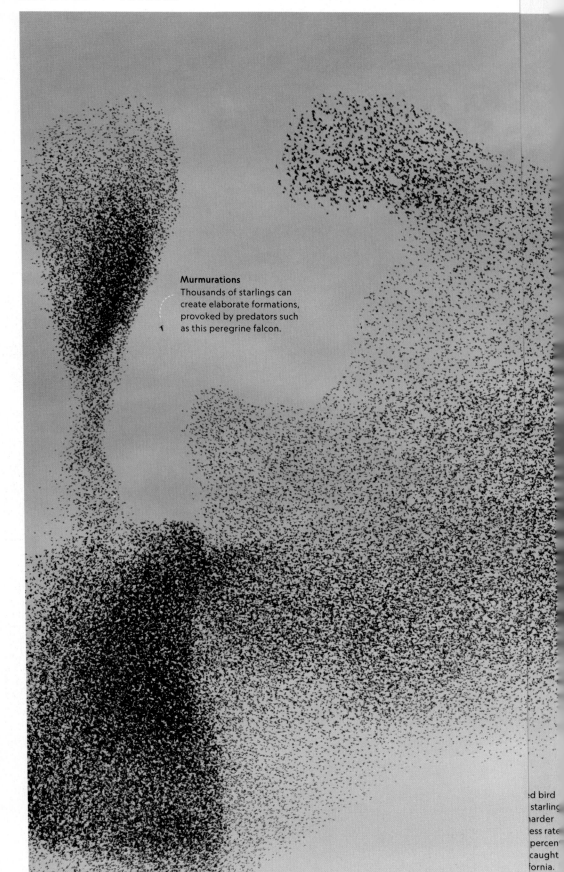

Murmurations
Thousands of starlings can
create elaborate formations,
provoked by predators such
as this peregrine falcon.

d bird
starlin
arder
ess rate
percen
caught
fornia.

AERIAL ACROBATICS

BY **DIANA MARQUES**
PHOTOGRAPH BY **NICK DUNLOP**

Look up on a fall or winter day in the Northern Hemisphere and you might see a cloud of starlings swirling over their roosts. These movements are called murmurations, for the murmur-like sound of thousands of wings flapping at once. Photographer Nick Dunlop estimates that this convergence of tens of thousands of starlings was a quarter mile at its widest and several hundred feet tall. The purpose of the shape-shifting phenomenon remains a mystery; it may afford a feeding advantage or a defense against predators—but can also end up attracting them.

SEE FLOCKS OF STARLINGS SWIRL IN VIDEOS AND SIMULATIONS AT *NATGEO.COM/MURMURATIONS*.

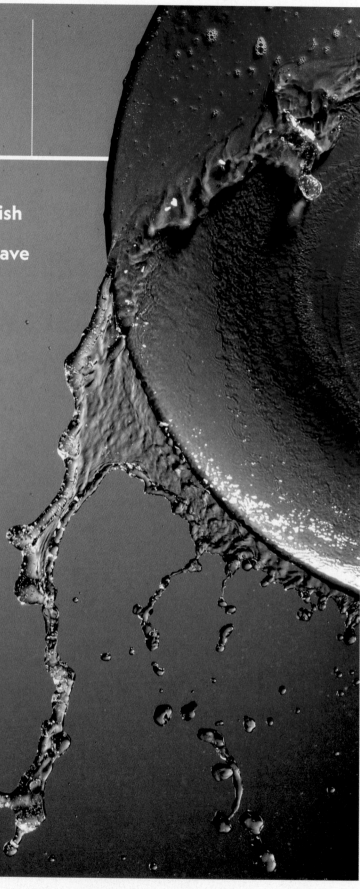

PLANET
P O S S I B L E

For more stories about how
to help the planet, go to
natgeo.com/planet

When mealtime dish duty calls, follow these five tips to save water and energy.

BY **CHRISTINA NUNEZ**

Skip the sink wash

If you have a dishwasher, use it. Running a full load typically uses a fraction of the water and generates less than half the greenhouse gases compared to most hand-washing methods.

Upgrade your dishwasher

In the United States, the most efficient ones carry the Energy Star label. Some machines use just 2.3 gallons of water for a full wash cycle—about the same amount you'd use in one minute of running the kitchen tap.

Scrape, don't rinse

It can be a hard habit to break, but you don't need to run your dishes under the faucet before putting them on the dishwashing rack. If there's dried-on debris, use the dishwasher's rinse feature instead of doing it yourself.

Let the dishes air-dry

When you press start, be sure your dishwasher's heated dry feature is off. Thanks to the energy saved, you'll lower the carbon footprint of the cycle by more than 10 percent.

Wash wisely

Of course, some dishwashing jobs require elbow grease. If you do hand-wash, turn off the tap while you scrub and use two filled basins: one with hot, soapy water for washing and another with cool water for rinsing.

When you choose paper products, you're playing a part in a circle of caring that shows nature some heart.

When you choose paper products, you create a healthy market for forest products, which in turn encourages forest owners to plant more trees. We grow twice as much timber as we use. Today, U.S. forestlands are strong. In the past 30 years, forest area has increased by nearly 33 million acres.

CHOOSE PAPER & PAPER PACKAGING AND BE A FORCE FOR NATURE
Learn more @ paperfornature.com

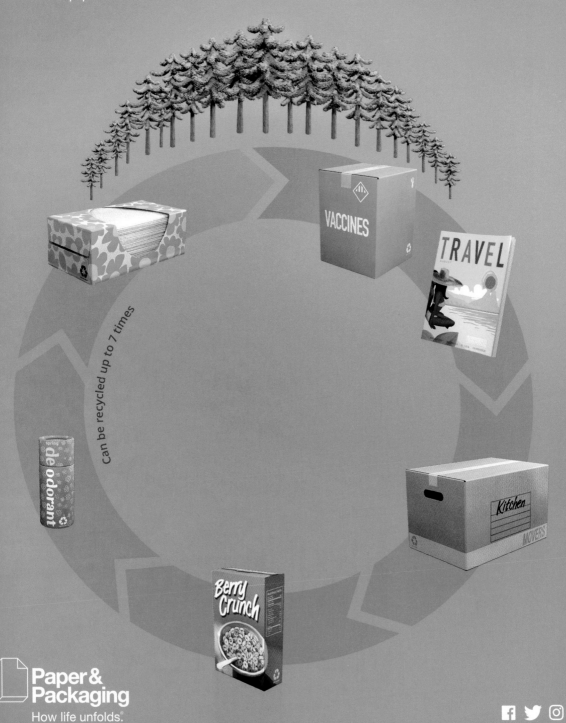

Can be recycled up to 7 times

Paper & Packaging
How life unfolds.®

Polar bear guard Trude Hohle checks for a safe path across the sea ice during a 2019 scientific expedition in the Arctic Ocean.

Extreme Measures

DRIFTING WITH AN ICE FLOE
IN THE POLAR NIGHT, A
PHOTOGRAPHER ON AN ARCTIC
RESEARCH EXPEDITION
DISCOVERS PROFOUND BEAUTY—
AND HER OWN LIMITATIONS.

STORY AND PHOTOGRAPHS BY
ESTHER HORVATH

THE ICEBREAKER *POLARSTERN* floated on the transpolar drift stream, frozen in sea ice, for nearly a year. On board were about a hundred scientists and crew members who were braving the polar winter to study climate change in the Arctic. I was there too, photographing the first leg of the MOSAiC expedition—the Multidisciplinary drifting Observatory for the Study of Arctic Climate. It was the longest and largest Arctic expedition in history and, for me, a gift from the universe.

Four years earlier I'd fallen under the spell of the ice and cold on my first Arctic assignment. When I returned home, I vowed to devote my photography to the fragile polar environment that had mesmerized me. Shortly afterward I heard about MOSAiC and knew I had to go.

By the time the *Polarstern* set sail from Tromsø, Norway, on September 20, 2019, I'd been on nine other polar expeditions. MOSAiC was different. For one thing, the first few legs took place during the long polar night. For another, help was very far away. The ship, intentionally trapped in an ice floe, drifted close to the North Pole during winter, when the ice was thickest. If anything had gone wrong, it would have taken two or three weeks for help to arrive and then two or three more weeks to return to human habitation. We had to be prepared to handle everything ourselves— from fire to falling into frigid water to heart attacks. (Toothaches were dealt with preemptively: I was told to have my wisdom teeth removed before the trip.)

Training began long before the expedition. Subjected to worst-case scenarios, we were taught how to get through them. During a simulated storm in a training pool, we jumped into rough water and swam through crashing waves to a life raft. We couldn't see except for occasional flashes of lightning; the deafening wind and thunder prevented us from communicating with each other. During polar bear safety training, we practiced shooting a rifle and a flare gun in complete darkness while people screamed around us. Some days I was so tired I cried.

I did every training twice—once as a participant and once as a photographer. The hardest was the firefighting. We learned how to put out fires and rescue people—all while wearing 66 pounds of gear in a controlled-burn training room where temperatures neared 250°F. For each exercise, participants spent about 10 minutes in the room. When I was photographing them, I stayed there for hours, holding my heavy camera with sweat dripping down my body. After it was over, I collapsed against a wall.

Yet I enjoyed it. It felt important to learn how to take care of myself and my colleagues in extreme conditions—and to learn what my limits were. I even volunteered for sea survival training, during which 14 of us were left for a few days on Svalbard, a Norwegian archipelago. We had to figure out how to distribute our limited supplies (only five sleeping bags), get water, and protect ourselves from the area's 3,000 polar bears. By the end, I was exhausted but strangely comfortable with the upcoming expedition. I knew I was prepared.

We arrived at the ice floe that was to be our home on October 4, one of the last days the sun rose above the horizon. Very soon the days passed in darkness. The moon and the stars were often covered by clouds. The only light came from the *Polarstern*'s spotlight and the headlamps worn by the participants.

Photographing was difficult. Wind and blowing snow made it hard to see through the camera's viewfinder, especially when I was wearing goggles. My hands became painfully cold. Many times I saw a beautiful moment but couldn't capture it because my hands weren't working. Eventually I covered my camera, including the trigger, with a very thin foam tape that allowed me to operate it while wearing mittens.

Every day I had to remind myself that I wasn't on land. Only two to three feet of unsteady ice lay between me and the ocean below. Under the lights from the ship, the ice appeared gray; the sky was pure black. It made me think of the famous NASA pictures taken from the moon in which you can see the lunar surface and then the universe in the background. From the ice I could see the universe. Those were the days I enjoyed most.

But the darkness also held terrors, which for me meant polar bears. On my second—and last—day as a polar bear guard on the ice, I stood alone with my rifle outside a tent where two scientists were working. There was too much wind, too much snow, and too

much darkness to see anything, even an eight-foot-tall polar bear. But I remembered that a trip wire had been installed around the science station. If a polar bear ambled through, a signal would flare.

As I was having that thought, an orange signal shot into the air. My next thought: The polar bear is scared, and it's running straight toward me. I tried to take out my signal pistol to scare the bear away—our goal was to protect the bears as well as ourselves—but my hands were so frozen I couldn't do it. One of the scientists grabbed it for me. By the time we made it back to the ship, I was shaking. Later the crew determined that the wind had tripped the wire. Even so, I decided that from then on I would shoot only with my camera.

On December 13 we saw a ship on the horizon: the icebreaker *Kapitan Dranitsyn*, coming to drop off the next team and pick us up. The return to Tromsø took 16 days, often through thick ice.

About a week after my return I was in Washington, D.C., for National Geographic's Storytellers Summit. As I walked through the city streets one morning, I had a sudden realization: I couldn't fall through the ice into the ocean here. I didn't have to scan the horizon for polar bears. I was safe. In that moment I understood how vigilant I'd become and how much fear I had felt. And yet, I missed the darkness so much. □

Esther Horvath, a Germany-based photographer who documents polar regions, chronicled communal life at a Greenland science station for the September 2019 issue.

For winter legs of the MOSAiC expedition, mandatory training prepared members for emergencies including falling into the frigid Arctic water. A participant is hauled out of a pool after swimming through the crashing waves and howling winds of a simulated storm.

UPPER CLASS JUST GOT LOWER PRICED

Finally, luxury built for value— not for false status

Until Stauer came along, you needed an inheritance to buy a timepiece with class and refinement. Not any more. The Stauer *Magnificat II* embodies the impeccable quality and engineering once found only in the watch collections of the idle rich. Today, it can be on your wrist.

The *Magnificat II* has the kind of thoughtful design that harkens back to those rare, 150-year-old moon phases that once could only be found under glass in a collector's trophy room.

Powered by 27 jewels, the *Magnificat II* is wound by the movement of your body. An exhibition back reveals the genius of the engineering and lets you witness the automatic rotor that enables you to wind the watch with a simple flick of your wrist.

It took three years of development and $26 million in advanced Swiss-built watch-making machinery to create the *Magnificat II*. When we took the watch to renowned watchmaker and watch historian George Thomas, he disassembled it and studied the escapement, balance wheel and the rotor. He remarked on the detailed guilloche face, gilt winding crown, and the crocodile-embossed leather band. He was intrigued by the three interior dials for day, date, and 24-hour moon phases. He estimated that this fine timepiece would cost over $2,500. We all smiled and told him that the Stauer price was less than $100. A truly magnificent watch at a truly magnificent price!

Try the *Magnificat II* for 30 days and if you are not receiving compliments, please return the watch for a full refund of the purchase price. The precision-built movement carries a 2 year warranty against defect. If you trust your own good taste, the *Magnificat II* is built for you.

The Stauer Magnificat II is powered by your own movement

Stauer Magnificat II Timepiece $399*

Offer Code Price **$99** + S&P **SAVE $300!**

You must use the offer code to get our special price.

1-800-333-2045

Your Offer Code: MAG581-08

 ACCREDITED BUSINESS
Rating of A+

- **Luxurious gold-finished case with exposition back**
- **27-jeweled automatic movement**
- **Croc-embossed band fits wrists 6¾"–8½"**
- **Water-resistant to 3 ATM**

† *Special price only for customers using the offer code versus the price on Stauer.com without your offer code.*

Stauer® 14101 Southcross Drive W., Ste 155, Dept. MAG581-08
Burnsville, Minnesota 55337 **www.stauer.com**

Stauer... *Afford the Extraordinary.*®

TRAVEL BEYOND YOUR WILDEST DREAMS

Listen for the thundering hooves of the great wildebeest migration on an unforgettable wildlife safari with National Geographic Expeditions. When you're ready to travel again, our experts, scientists, and storytellers will bring you closer to the wonders of the wild than you ever dreamed possible.

NATIONAL GEOGRAPHIC
EXPEDITIONS

To learn more about all our trips and to request a **FREE** catalog
NATGEOEXPEDITIONS.COM/WILDLIFE | 1-888-351-3274

FEATURES

122

AT A PRIMATE REHABILITATION CENTER IN THE DEMOCRATIC REPUBLIC OF THE CONGO, STAFF HELPING CHIMPS RECOVER FIND THAT THE ANIMALS HELP THEM IN RETURN.

PHOTO: BRENT STIRTON

THE **FUTURE**

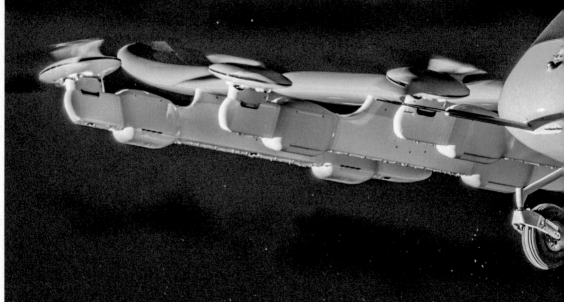

A GREEN REVOLUTION IN TRAVEL HAS BEGUN.
MODERN BATTERY-POWERED CARS ARE SELLING FAST,
AND ZERO-EMISSION PLANES ARE COMING.

BY LAND PAGE 43   **BY AIR** PAGE 64

IS **ELECTRIC**

BY LAND

THE BIG BET ON CLEAN CARS

AT VOLKSWAGEN'S ASSEMBLY PLANT in Chattanooga, Tennessee, car bodies soar high above the concrete floor on conveyors, like seats on a slow-moving carnival ride. Every 73 seconds one gets lowered onto a power train, and soon body and chassis begin rising together. As I watch, workers in roller chairs carrying pistol-shaped power wrenches glide beneath a Passat sailing by at chest height. They fasten rock guards and skid plates to the undercarriage before holstering their tools to await the next car.

BY **CRAIG WELCH**

PHOTOGRAPHS BY **DAVID GUTTENFELDER**

Across 3.4 million square feet, about 3,800 workers and 1,500 robots move in this stop-and-go rhythm all day, building some of the most recognizable gasoline-powered vehicles on the road—45 an hour, 337 per shift, more than 1.1 million since Volkswagen finished the plant in 2011.

This site has a complicated history: Beginning in World War II and periodically for the next three decades, military contractors processed nitric and sulfuric acid here to make TNT, storing the munitions in concrete bunkers in nearby forests. Toxic fumes from the factory scalded petunias and yellowed pine needles for miles. But today, in a city that once had America's worst air pollution, on a former weapons site that contributed mightily to those filthy skies, a car company with its own messy legacy on emissions—Volkswagen cheated on pollution rules for seven years—is trying to help green the nation's transportation system.

Soon this plant will roll out Volkswagen's first U.S.-built electric vehicle. In 2022, it will begin mass-producing the car, a compact SUV called the ID.4, on its existing assembly line, splicing production between gas-powered models so that it can respond nimbly to changing demand. On my visit to the plant, the transition is well under way. A team of Volkswagen logistics experts ticks off the dizzying alterations as we tour the line.

All-electric vehicles are simpler than gas-powered ones.

The National Geographic Society, committed to illuminating and protecting the wonder of our world, has funded Explorer David Guttenfelder's storytelling about the human condition since 2014.

ILLUSTRATION BY JOE MCKENDRY

Automakers have made great strides in developing climate-friendly vehicles. Just a month after Ford unveiled an electric version of the popular F-150 pickup, customers had reserved more than 100,000 of them. The base price for an F-150 Lightning is $40,000, about $10,000 above the gas-powered original, but Ford says the electric model will cost much less to maintain.

An electric Volkswagen ID.3 rides an elevator in a storage tower in Dresden, Germany, after being assembled. Battered by an emissions cheating scandal, the Volkswagen group now plans to spend

more than $40 billion to design 70 new electric-vehicle models, including the ID.4, which will be built for U.S. consumers at Volkswagen's plant in Chattanooga, Tennessee.

They have no gas tanks, no pistons, no spark plugs—and no tailpipe. "The basic idea is, there's less parts," assembly specialist Chris Rehrig shouts to me over the plant's whir and hum.

On the other hand, they have enormous batteries. At Volkswagen, battery packs weighing more than 1,000 pounds will be assembled across the street and carted in on self-driving vehicles. Each battery pack, sheathed in a plate veined with cooling fluid, will be bolted by automated screw gun to a car's underbody. The same machine, when a gas-powered car approaches, will instead screw in a heat shield. Making all this work smoothly will take "a bit of a dance," says Rehrig's supervisor, Noah Walker, with a hint of weariness.

That Volkswagen and so many others are now attempting such a dance suggests that we've reached a crucial moment for the planet. This company, and this industry, are pivoting away from what made Volkswagen the world's largest manufacturing company by revenue: the carbon dioxide-belching internal combustion engine.

As more people and governments push for urgent action on climate change, cars and trucks are undergoing their greatest makeover since the automobile's inception more than a century ago. Start-ups and standard-bearers alike are fighting for a toehold in what industry leaders suddenly see as their best path forward: vehicles without tailpipe emissions. By almost every measure, their popularity is surging. Virtually overnight, the era of the electric car has arrived.

And yet, by the timetable needed to address the climate challenge, the transition away from gas-powered vehicles remains far too slow. Global temperature records keep getting crushed as greenhouse gas pollution rises, fueling punishing droughts and wildfires from the Arctic to Australia. Melting ice sheets are raising sea levels, increasing flooding just as storms grow more extreme. To avoid peril for millions of people, the Intergovernmental Panel on Climate Change says, the world needs to bring carbon dioxide emissions to zero by 2050, preferably much sooner.

With nearly a quarter of global emissions coming from all types of transportation, can we wean ourselves off petrol-powered cars fast enough to avoid the worst effects? And can we do it without sparking a new environmental calamity? Several upstart companies and quite a few from the stodgy old guard are now betting their future—and ours—that millions of consumers are finally ready to make the switch.

Colorfully decorated buses called *matatus* ferry passengers through the streets of Nairobi, Kenya. One company, Opibus, is removing combustion engines from matatus and replacing them with battery-powered motors. In Kenya and across the developing world, small start-ups are trying to find inexpensive ways to make transportation cleaner.
NICHOLE SOBECKI

IT'S HARD TO ARGUE THAT what we're witnessing is anything less than a revolution. In the 1990s, General Motors introduced an electric car, built fewer than 1,200, and recalled them. Today the pace of change is blistering.

The number of all-electric and plug-in-hybrid electric vehicles, or EVs, rose by nearly half last year, even as car sales overall fell 16 percent. The types of models available to drivers worldwide increased 40 percent, to about 370. In North America, the variety is slated to nearly triple by 2024, to 138. Already there are electric Mini Coopers, Porsches, and Harley-Davidsons.

Governments from California to China, Japan, and the United Kingdom recently announced plans to ban sales of new passenger vehicles

powered solely by gas or diesel by 2035 or sooner. Automotive giants from Volvo to Jaguar now say they'll phase out piston engines by then anyway, while Ford says its passenger vehicles in Europe will be all EVs or hybrids in five years and all electric by 2030. GM has pledged to be carbon-neutral by 2040. President Joe Biden has vowed to transition the federal fleet of more than 600,000 vehicles to EVs, and his administration plans to tighten fuel-efficiency standards.

Wall Street and investors are betting big. For a while last year Tesla, responsible for almost 80 percent of all U.S. EV sales in 2020, was worth more than oil giants ExxonMobil, Chevron, Shell, and BP—combined. New electric-car and electric-truck companies keep popping up:

Bollinger, Faraday Future, Nio, Byton. Others are coming on strong. A two-door electric micro-car with a top speed of 62 miles an hour and a sale price that starts below $6,000 has been outselling Tesla in China, home to more than 40 percent of the world's plug-in vehicles.

The days of light-duty combustion engines finally, truly, seem numbered. "The dam is breaking; the tipping point is here," says Sam Ricketts, a member of the team that wrote Washington governor Jay Inslee's climate action plan during his presidential run. Many of Inslee's ideas later found their way into Biden's climate plans.

"Electrifying transportation is our future. I think that train has left the station," says Kristin Dziczek, an economist with the Center for

CHARGING AHEAD

All-electric cars and plug-in hybrids (EVs) are just 4 percent of global car sales today. That will change with increased governmental support, improvements in battery cost and technology, more public and private charging ports, and new electric versions of popular car and truck models.

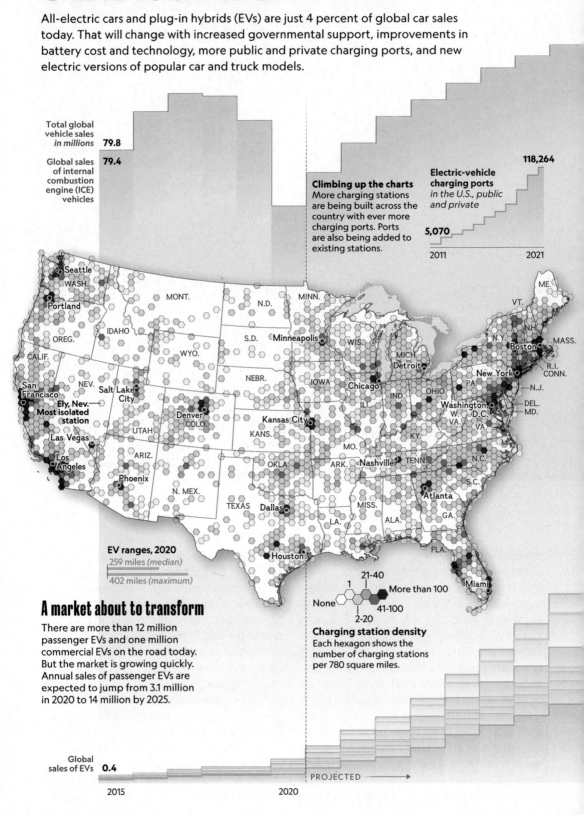

Total global vehicle sales *in millions* **79.8**

Global sales of internal combustion engine (ICE) vehicles **79.4**

Climbing up the charts
More charging stations are being built across the country with ever more charging ports. Ports are also being added to existing stations.

Electric-vehicle charging ports *in the U.S., public and private*

118,264

5,070

2011   2021

EV ranges, 2020
259 miles *(median)*
402 miles *(maximum)*

Ely, Nev.—Most isolated station

A market about to transform

There are more than 12 million passenger EVs and one million commercial EVs on the road today. But the market is growing quickly. Annual sales of passenger EVs are expected to jump from 3.1 million in 2020 to 14 million by 2025.

Charging station density
Each hexagon shows the number of charging stations per 780 square miles.

None | 1 | 2-20 | 21-40 | 41-100 | More than 100

Global sales of EVs **0.4**

2015   2020   PROJECTED →

Map shows data for the contiguous U.S. In Alaska, Juneau has the most charging stations with 15 in 780 square miles. In Hawaii, Honolulu has the most with 189 in 780 square miles.

97
Total

31
ICE
vehicles

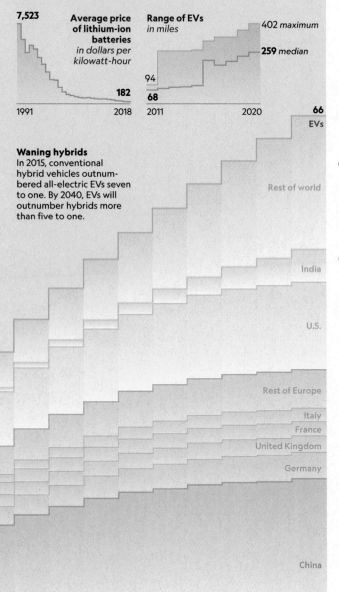

Lower prices, longer distances

Battery prices have decreased 97 percent since 1991 and are expected to fall even further as production scales up. In 2020, the Tesla Model S Long Range Plus was the first all-electric vehicle to reach a maximum range of more than 400 miles.

7,523

Average price of lithium-ion batteries
in dollars per kilowatt-hour

182

1991   2018

Range of EVs
in miles

402 *maximum*

259 *median*

94

68

2011   2020

66
EVs

Waning hybrids

In 2015, conventional hybrid vehicles outnumbered all-electric EVs seven to one. By 2040, EVs will outnumber hybrids more than five to one.

Rest of world

India

U.S.

Rest of Europe

Italy

France

United Kingdom

Germany

China

Breaking down the surge

Industry experts predict that global sales of EVs could rise to 70 percent of the passenger car market by 2040. China, the U.S., and European countries are projected to be among the leaders; the developing world will likely shift to EVs more slowly.

Rest of the world: slower growth
Policy support (such as subsidies) for EVs is limited, and combustion vehicles are more affordable. But EVs will proliferate as they become cheaper.

EVs as share of total sales by year
2019: **0%**   2040: **77%**

India: obstacles and incentives
Exemptions on road taxes and registration fees incentivize ownership of electric cars, scooters, and rickshaws. A dearth of charging stations remains an obstacle.

2019: **0%**   2040: **53%**

U.S.: accelerating quickly
With home garages common, Americans can more easily recharge electric cars. By the mid-2020s, many two-car households are projected to have at least one EV.

2019: **2%**   2040: **74%**

Europe: saturating the market
The EV share of the auto market in some of the continent's more prosperous countries is soaring already. In Germany, it could reach 90 percent by 2040.

2019: **4%**   2040: **78%**

China: plans to expand
Ambitious policies include subsidies, rebates for charging costs, and traffic restriction waivers. China has one public charging port per five EVs, compared with 20 ports in the U.S.

2019: **5%**   2040: **77%**

2040

JASON TREAT, EVE CONANT, AND MATTHEW W. CHWASTYK, NGM STAFF; KELSEY NOWAKOWSKI
SOURCES: BLOOMBERGNEF; ALTERNATIVE FUELS DATA CENTER, U.S. DEPT. OF ENERGY VEHICLE
TECHNOLOGIES OFFICE; MICAH S. ZIEGLER AND JESSIKA E. TRANCIK, MIT

An electric-converted Toyota Land Cruiser is test-driven at Kenya's Ngong Hills Wind Power Station. Renewables now make up more than two-thirds of the energy in the country, which has set ambitious

targets for reducing its carbon dioxide emissions. Greening transportation would be a major step. In Kenya, most cars, trucks, and motorcycles are imported as used vehicles and run on gas or diesel.

Automotive Research, a Michigan-based organization partially backed by car manufacturers.

How did we get here?

Even before Toyota successfully mass-produced the Prius hybrid more than two decades ago, some climate-conscious nations had begun tightening emissions standards. Countries such as Norway, where half the new vehicles on the road in 2020 were electric, started offering tax savings for electric cars. In China, cities with air pollution problems made it faster and cheaper to register EVs than vehicles with internal combustion engines. The U.S. government offered consumers up to $7,500 off the purchase of EVs and hybrids and sank research and development money into batteries. Then,

in 2009, Tesla got a $465 million Department of Energy loan to jump-start production of sedans. Battery prices fell 89 percent in the next 10 years, and Tesla went on to sell 1.5 million plug-ins.

Yet there is a long way to go. Roughly 12 million plug-in cars and trucks have been sold globally, nearly 90 percent of them in just three regions: China, Europe, and the United States. But some 1.5 billion gas-guzzlers still crowd the roads, and the total number of passenger vehicles of all kinds may grow by another billion in the next 30 years, as incomes rise in underdeveloped countries.

Whether drivers across the globe adopt EVs quickly depends on several factors. Industry is whittling away at some of the biggest barriers to

Batteries are the heart of electric vehicles, and automakers are trying to make them lighter, faster charging, and longer lasting. At a plant in Normal, Illinois, workers for electric-vehicle start-up Rivian hand-assemble battery packs the length of the undercarriage for preproduction vehicles. Batteries are machine-made for models in production. The company is building electric pickups, sport utility vehicles, and delivery vans.

accelerate this transition. No one expects the variety of options for consumers to match today's gas-powered cars soon. Government incentives, such as renewal of the $7,500 tax credit, which is no longer available for some automakers, may be essential to attracting buyers.

"There isn't a market in the world that can do this without some kind of public investment," Dziczek says. The Biden administration wants to spend $15 billion to help add 500,000 charging stations, but many in Congress have balked.

The price and sustainability of EVs also depend on raw materials. EV batteries rely on lithium, nickel, cobalt, manganese, and graphite. Most of those materials are mined in just a few places, and much of it is refined in China. With demand surging, EV-manufacturing nations are scrambling to secure supplies—there are plans for a lithium mine in Nevada, for example. But "there's no point in having a lithium mine in America, shipping the lithium out to Asia for processing, then shipping it back to America for use in your batteries," says Jonathon Mulcahy of the research firm Rystad Energy, which projects potential lithium shortages later this decade.

At the same time, extraction of these metals has led to ecological and human rights abuses. Governments such as the European Union are wrestling with ways to make supply chains stable, ethical, and safe, while automakers, including Volkswagen, are establishing auditing and certification systems to make sure battery suppliers comply with environment and labor rules. Consumers may hesitate to trust such commitments, however. Automakers have disappointed them before.

entry for consumers: range, recharging times, charging infrastructure, cost. A lab prototype of a solid-state battery may be the first step toward recharging electric vehicles in just 10 minutes. Tesla and Lucid Motors are already building all-electric vehicles that could exceed 400 miles per charge. Lucid claims its car will top 500, while Aptera maintains that some drivers of its three-wheeled, aerodynamic, sun-powered machine may never need to visit a charging station. For now, most new EVs are luxury cars that few can afford. But investment bank UBS and research firm BloombergNEF predict that electric cars could reach cost parity with conventional vehicles in five years or so.

Still, analysts insist more needs to happen to

WHEN THINGS GO WRONG on Volkswagen's Chattanooga assembly line—if tools or parts break—workers yank cords that grind production to a halt, and one of a few easily recognized songs blares across the factory floor. Managers use these tunes to quickly identify the holdup. During my tour, I heard Scott Joplin's "The Entertainer" and noticed things around me had stopped moving. But there was a lot going on that day. The special robots needed to make EVs already had been installed. Buyers were locking in new parts suppliers; executives were readying for a hiring binge of hundreds more workers.

The seeds of this moment were planted in 1979, when Tennessee governor Lamar Alexander flew

AN ECLECTIC
ELECTRIC HISTORY

Hardly a product of the modern age, electric cars evolved alongside those powered by the internal combustion engine. The height of their popularity was at the turn of the 20th century, when they were a third of all vehicles on the road.

The Jedlik model electric car

1828
Hungarian priest and physicist Ányos Jedlik invents an early version of the direct-current motor and builds a model to demonstrate its potential.

1859
French physicist Gaston Planté invents the first rechargeable battery.

The Trouvé electric tricycle on the streets of Paris

1881
French electrical engineer Gustave Trouvé fits an electric motor and rechargeable battery to a tricycle, creating the first roadworthy electric vehicle.

to Japan with maps and a satellite photograph. There he convinced the chairman of Nissan that his state offered ideal manufacturing land linked by rail and highway to major population centers on both coasts. Other carmakers followed—and today, this conservative state is a player in the move to climate-friendly cars.

Since 2013, the Nissan plant in Smyrna, outside Nashville, has built the electric Leaf, the world's first commercially successful modern EV. At less than $25,000 after tax credits, it remains one of North America's cheapest. Forty miles away, GM is spending two billion dollars to redesign its Spring Hill factory so it can assemble an electric Cadillac, the first of several EVs that will be built there. By 2023, that entire operation will be solar powered. The company also is investing $2.3 billion in a battery plant that will employ 1,300. The Tennessee Valley Authority, which runs hydroelectric dams and other power plants, plans to fund fast-charging stations every 50 miles along Tennessee's freeways.

Then there's Chattanooga. In 1969, a year before the Environmental Protection Agency was created, the U.S. government declared the city's particulate-matter pollution the worst in the country. Its ozone pollution was second only to Los Angeles. Decades of revitalization led to one of the most celebrated environmental achievements in history. In 2008, not long after the city finally had met ozone standards, Volkswagen broke ground on its new plant.

The Volkswagen Group, which includes Audi, Porsche, and nine other carmakers, has embraced EVs. In part that's because of the emissions scandal, revealed in 2014, which led to billions of dollars in fines, the recall of millions of cars, and the indictment of its former CEO on conspiracy charges. A settlement with the EPA for installing devices on some 590,000 diesels sold in the U.S. that made them appear less polluting required the company to make huge investments in EV charging. But that alone doesn't explain the depth of Volkswagen's conversion.

The company is investing more than $40 billion worldwide to design 70 new electric models and produce 26 million by 2030. With partners, VW expects to install 3,500 fast chargers in the U.S. by year's end, and 18,000 in Europe by 2025. Volkswagen has pumped $300 million into a battery start-up that hopes to cut charging times in half. It's building and expanding battery plants across Europe, aiming to halve battery prices.

"Credit where credit is due: It is absolutely clear that VW, among the large automakers, is by far making the largest investments in EVs," says Nic Lutsey, director of the electric-vehicle program for the International Council on Clean Transportation, which produces data and analysis to help governments green transportation. It was Lutsey's organization that caught Volkswagen cheating on emissions. "Those investments have them on a path far greater than what is required" by any legal settlement, Lutsey says.

Scott Keogh, CEO of Volkswagen Group of America, grew up in the 1970s on Long Island, squishing into the wayback of his family's VW Beetle. He studied comparative literature in college and worked on development projects in Bolivia before finding his way into the auto business, first at Mercedes-Benz and later at Audi. In 2018, after the EPA settlement, he took over VW's North American business.

The emissions scandal is "a corporate disaster, and certainly a bruise and a scar, if you will, that we will have with us," Keogh says when I connect with him by Skype. But "the company came together and said, 'What do we do? Do we just survive this crisis? And maybe move a little effort here or tweak a little bit there and just kind of survive it? Or do we come out of this crisis stronger, better, smarter, and with a purpose?' And thank goodness the company selected the latter."

Volkswagen announced its commitment to EVs so early that when it presented the plan to U.S. car dealers, Keogh tells me, "I would say, overwhelmingly, it was met with ... cynicism, I think, would probably be the appropriate word." Even just a few years ago, dealers presumed EVs would remain a mere niche.

All that has changed, Keogh says. Research regularly reaches his desk suggesting that under some optimistic scenarios, car buying could be 50 percent electric within the decade. Suddenly, VW's bets look "downright smart—and downright necessary," Keogh says.

He doesn't underestimate the challenge, however. Less than 5 percent of new-car sales in Europe today are all-electric vehicles; in the U.S., it's 2 percent. (The number rises to 8 percent in China.) "And of course, we're making investments and making projections that are going to put it, in 10 years, somewhere, let's say 30 to 40 percent," Keogh says. Counting on such a rapid growth curve is "something that's certainly capable of keeping you up at night."

In 1899, the Belgian La Jamais Contente becomes the first EV to exceed 60 miles an hour.

1890s
The first commercial EVs are sold; in Belgium, Henri Pieper develops one of the first hybrid cars.

1900
In this year, 40 percent of American cars are powered by steam, 38 percent by electricity, and 22 percent by internal combustion engine.

1910s to 1930s
Cheaper oil and combustion models drive EVs out of the market.

1980s
Lithium-ion batteries with more power are developed, reigniting interest in EVs as ranges increase.

1990
California's mandate to ramp up sales of zero-emission cars sparks a new generation of EVs.

1997
The popular Toyota Prius kick-starts the modern hybrid-vehicle market.

Tesla Model 3s in a Japanese port

2008
The Tesla Roadster, with a range of 245 miles, launches a wave of high-performance EVs.

But that's also why Keogh doesn't view Tesla or other EV producers as his chief competitors. The drivers he's targeting are the ones shopping now for small gas-powered SUVs, such as Toyota's RAV4 or Subaru's Forester. "We're laser focused on the 98 percent of the market that is not driving an electric vehicle."

A SIMILAR BATTLE FOR CONSUMERS' HEARTS happened at the beginning too. In 1896, when horses and buggies were still competing with automobiles, prospective buyers at the first big car show in London could choose between electric and gas power. Some aspects of that choice haven't changed.

"Electricity has the advantage that it works without smell and with less noise and vibration," the *British Medical Journal* wrote in a review of the show, "but the disadvantage of the costliness of the accumulators [batteries], and the impossibility of recharging except where the electric supply is available."

When the first U.S. auto dealership opened in Detroit a few years later, it sold only electric cars. In Austria, Ferdinand Porsche's early designs also relied on electricity. His partner, Ludwig Lohner, said he favored electric drives because he found the air in Vienna already "ruthlessly spoiled by the large number of petrol engines." But cheap oil and paved rural roads would soon cement a victor. Electric vehicles would be gone by the end of the 1930s.

In Normal, Illinois, I meet a man with a distinctive vision for how to bring them back. In 2015, Mitsubishi shut down its auto plant here, laying off close to 1,300 workers. Two years later, engineer and entrepreneur Robert "RJ" Scaringe converted the vacant space into a factory for his start-up, Rivian.

Tall and thin, in his late 30s, Scaringe is understated. I first glimpse him, in untucked flannel, standing alone in line at the cafeteria on a day when his company's value is nearly $28 billion.

Even as a Florida teen tinkering on Porsches in a neighbor's garage, Scaringe knew he wanted to make cars. When he was at MIT, where he got a doctorate in mechanical engineering, worry about climate change consumed him. As we stroll through the old Mitsubishi plant, before Rivian's new vehicles are in production, Scaringe explains the task as he sees it: "How do we take roughly 90 to 100 million cars a year and get those to be electric?"

With mentoring from car buffs and automotive engineers, a group of Detroit teenagers is converting a 1955 Buick into a battery-powered hot rod. The program is designed to teach mechanical and racing skills, as well as demonstrate the potential of EVs. As team lead Andy Didorosi says, "Electric cars are thought of as an appliance. We're here to show people that they can shred as well—or better—than their gas counterparts."

Scaringe decided his contribution would be to design EVs drivers might desire. And what do consumers want most? Some of the least efficient vehicles on the road. There are now more than 200 million SUVs worldwide, six times as many as a decade ago, and millions more trucks. In the U.S., together the two were 70 percent of the new-vehicle market in 2019. "Not only is it the biggest problem in terms of carbon and sustainability ... but they're also the most popular vehicle type," Scaringe says.

Rivian's first two EVs, a short-bed pickup called the R1T and an SUV called the R1S, will offer green alternatives for the outdoor set. Like Tesla, the company is building its own exclusive charging network: 3,500 fast chargers on

highways, and thousands more in state parks and near trailheads. Scaringe felt he had no choice. Even though most charging takes place at home, a spotty and inconsistent charging network complicates long trips, he says, and remains "a reason for someone not to buy the vehicle."

Rivian won't have the truck market to itself. Tesla has unveiled its Cybertruck, and an electric version of Ford's F-150—the most popular vehicle in America, with annual sales approaching 900,000 in 2019—is expected in 2022. The base price for the F-150 Lightning will be substantially less than Rivian's high-end vehicles. Within a month of its unveiling, more than 100,000 customers had made reservations.

Ford is an investor in Rivian, and Scaringe is sanguine about competition; he's quick to point out that a wholesale transition to EVs can't be achieved by any one company. But he and his team also see our relationship with vehicles changing in ways that could help electrification.

"Fifteen years ago, if we wanted bananas, we'd go to the store. If I wanted new shoes, I'd drive to the store," he says. Now, deliveries bring books and meals and groceries and shoes to our door. Others make trips for us. In that, Scaringe sees opportunity. What if he could switch a fleet of delivery trucks to EVs? "You may, as a customer, not yet choose to electrify on your personal vehicle. But because you're handing over a lot of your last-mile logistics, you now are going to be electrifying whether you realize it or not."

A global transportation revolution will require huge amounts of materials such as lithium, nickel, cobalt, manganese, and graphite to make batteries. In the fishing villages of Tapuemea and Tapunggaeya on

the island of Sulawesi in Indonesia, nickel mining has brought jobs with wages rivaling those of workers in Jakarta. But erosion and runoff after forests are cleared for mines can harm nearby sea life.

Rivian is making 100,000 electric delivery vehicles for Amazon, the retail giant. Some are on streets now being tested. FedEx also has announced that it will go electric. UPS took a stake in another EV company and is buying 10,000 electric delivery vans.

Scaringe is thinking beyond the U.S. to the developing world, where very few people own new cars and trucks, and relationships with vehicles are fundamentally different. He suspects new user models will emerge there: partial ownership, flexible leasing, subscription services.

Rather than watching new gas-powered vehicles take over places such as Africa and India, he says, "the right answer is to say, How can we innovate on the product, the business model, the ecosystem, to allow these markets to just skip what, you know, we in the U.S. or Europe or China went through? Which is these hugely inefficient, very dirty transportation ecosystems."

IN KENYA, ESTHER WAIRIMU is working on it. Deep in the heart of Nairobi's industrial district, rows of warehouses the size of soccer fields house coffee roasters, paintsellers, furniture makers. But down one dusty lane packed with trucks is a different kind of business.

On a spotless floor framed by crystal-clean white walls, 88 employees, including Wairimu, spend days soldering cables and testing battery systems, plugging into one of the first vehicle chargers in Kenya. When photographer Nichole Sobecki met Wairimu there last spring, the 25-year-old was troubleshooting wiring on a beat-up *matatu,* a small, decorated public bus. She was trying to help make it run on batteries.

Wairimu is an engineer at Opibus, one of many start-ups hoping to bring electrification to developing countries. But the four-year-old company isn't building cars or trucks. It's converting old petroleum-powered transit vehicles into EVs and building new, cheap electric motorcycles—and helping Kenyans finance them.

"At the moment, things here are not so developed," Wairimu tells me. "Many places in Africa don't even have gas stations. We have a chance to have a better vision." Though Opibus was founded by Swedish engineers, most Opibus employees, like Wairimu, are Kenyan, and 40 percent are women.

The developing world is a great untapped market, "but it's very scary for traditional vehicle makers," chief strategist Albin Wilson says.

Bikers on nearly silent electric motorcycles wind through a canyon above Malibu, California. The outing was organized by Harlan Flagg, owner of Hollywood Electrics, an electric-motorcycle shop that promotes the joy of riding quiet, clean bikes over rumbling, gas-fueled ones. Even Harley-Davidson now sells electric motorcycles.

And yet the time to act is now. The number of gas- and diesel-powered vehicles in parts of East Africa is roughly doubling each decade. Most of them—about 85 percent of all vehicles in Kenya—are older ones imported used. Kenya limits importation to vehicles no more than eight years old and has established pollution standards for new and used vehicles, but more than 80 other countries in the developing world have weak limits or none. Few major vehicle manufacturers are focused on this emerging market, so it's left to tiny outfits such as Opibus to try to lay the groundwork for change.

Opibus began by creating conversion kits for safari companies, subbing EV motors and batteries, which could be charged by solar panels,

into the skeletons of diesel jeeps. But company leaders wanted to make a bigger impact, so they moved on to building electric motorcycles.

They've field-tested a hundred so far. Each costs no more than a conventional motorcycle—and fuel and maintenance cost less than half. In a place where many owners use their bikes as taxis or delivery vehicles, that's appealing.

Those drivers tend to lack the attachment Americans have to petrol-powered vehicles, Wilson says. Their primary interest appears to be in whether electrification will make their lives better. "They want to know: Will this tool make me more money—yes or no?" Wilson says.

Rob de Jong, with the UN Environment Programme in Kenya, says similar efforts are popping up throughout the developing world. There are EV start-ups in Rwanda and Ethiopia. A city in the Philippines is experimenting with electric postal vehicles. Electric buses may come to the Seychelles. De Jong believes automakers should step up efforts to promote the trend.

The potential impact is great, Wairimu says. Climate change already threatens the rain-dependent agriculture that East Africa and her own family rely on. "If we go electric, we are really saving Africa," she tells Sobecki. "If we go electric, we are protecting the entire world." □

Staff writer **Craig Welch** and freelance photographer **David Guttenfelder** drove a series of electric cars on a road trip across the United States for an article that appeared in the April 2020 issue.

Once seen as boring and impractical, electric cars are embraced now even by drag-racing enthusiasts. In June, carmakers from EV West in San Marcos, California, test their Electraliner, built with a Tesla

motor and battery pack, in the Mojave Desert. They are aiming to break EV land-speed records. A previous version of their electric dragster averaged 229.363 miles an hour on two tests.

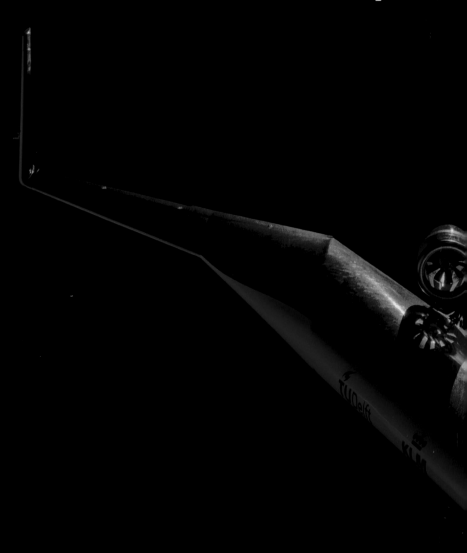

HOW GREEN,

SMALL, BATTERY-POWERED PLANES ARE ON THE WAY.
BUT BUILDING LARGE, ZERO-EMISSION AIRLINERS
IS A DAUNTING CHALLENGE.

HOW **SOON?**

BY AIR

THE GRAVITY PROBLEM

A FACT AND A FIGURE KEEP POPPING to mind as I talk with aviation experts about whether commercial flight can ever go green. The fact is this: Everything you can think of that's spurring a green revolution on the ground will be of little help in the sky anytime soon. Solar panels, wind turbines, electric engines, high-storage batteries, hydrogen fuel cells, magnetic levitation—they are all, bluntly put, useless at present when it comes to the technological challenge of launching a few hundred people into the stratosphere and carrying them thousands of miles. Here's the figure: More than 80 percent of humanity has never flown at all.

How this fact and this figure relate to each other is the crux of the problem facing airlines and aircraft manufacturers as they take on the critical task of decarbonizing flight. Aviation can go green, but not soon and not as comprehensively as ground-bound transport. Gravity is a very stubborn thing. Yet how quickly the air travel industry does proceed could affect its image—and bottom line. As environmental advocates warn that flying makes an intolerably large contribution to climate change, the pace of progress in greening the sky may well lead travelers to question whether it's ethical to fly at all.

"Look, we simply have to get there," says Jennifer Holmgren, chief executive officer of LanzaTech, a company pioneering the development of aviation fuel from unorthodox sources such as waste to replace the standard kerosene jet fuel. "Everyone agrees: Airplanes simply can't keep flying around on fossil kerosene. But there is no magic solution to this problem."

To be clear, promising developments with zero-emission, battery-powered electric engines are already happening in one area of aviation, involving trips of limited duration and distance. George Jetson's flying car is indeed on the way, albeit with AI and not George at the controls. Airlines specializing in short hops with small planes will lead the way to electric flight.

BY **SAM HOWE VERHOVEK**

PHOTOGRAPHS BY **DAVIDE MONTELEONE**

The National Geographic Society, committed to illuminating and protecting the wonder of our world, has funded Explorer Davide Monteleone's work about how transportation affects the environment.

ILLUSTRATION BY JOE MCKENDRY

A turbofan engine is inspected at a Rolls-Royce plant in Derby, England. Advances in design and materials have made today's jet engines more fuel efficient and cleaner burning than ever, but airplanes are a long way from being green. Rolls-Royce is developing an engine called the UltraFan that will be able to run entirely on sustainable fuels.

PREVIOUS PHOTO

Flying-V, developed at Delft University of Technology in the Netherlands, undergoes testing in a wind tunnel. The radical design, known as blended wing body, may prove to be 20 percent more efficient than conventional airplanes. Both Airbus and Boeing have tested similar models.

Engineers at Lilium in Munich, Germany, work near a full-scale model of the company's vertical takeoff and landing airplane, which is powered by 36 electric jet engines. It's designed to carry a pilot and six

passengers on trips up to 155 miles. Many companies are developing similar electric aircraft—some flown autonomously—for air taxi and regional flights, the first areas of aviation expected to go green.

But no battery yet invented can power, say, a Boeing 747 from New York to London. My favorite expert calculation comes from David Alexander, director of aerospace standards at SAE International, a transportation engineering association. He estimates it would take the juice of 4.4 million laptop batteries just to get airborne. Except that the jumbo jet could never leave the ground; the batteries would weigh seven times as much as the plane. Pound for pound, liquid fuel contains vastly more energy than even the most sophisticated battery in use today.

To the industry's credit, the average commercial flight will get greener every year, as it has consistently since the dawn of the jet age. "Evolution, not revolution" is a phrase I keep hearing, but the small improvements do add up. Today's jetliners are twice as fuel efficient and several times cleaner burning than their venerable ancestors. But that bright side obscures a darker one. The reality is that increasing air traffic outstrips such gains. On average, carbon emissions from flight keep contributing more to

human contribution to global warming today.

That figure will likely climb as passenger and freight air traffic grows while ground transportation and other activities such as construction become far more energy efficient. All this has led to a movement urging people not to fly or at least to fly a lot less, a campaign with a name that has caught on in Europe and is becoming familiar elsewhere: *flygskam,* a Swedish term best translated as "flight shame." For teenage activist Greta Thunberg and others doing the flygskam-ing, the case is simple but compelling.

"Hour for hour, there is just about nothing you as an individual can do that's worse for the health of the planet than to sit on an airplane," says Peter Kalmus, an astrophysicist turned NASA climate scientist who hasn't flown since 2012 and is the founder of *noflyclimatesci.org,* which showcases testimonies from scientists and others to fly less or not at all. "The hard fact that most people haven't accepted yet is that we don't need to fly, and if you truly accept that we are in a climate emergency, you shouldn't fly."

FLIGHT IS GETTING GREENER,
AND SMALL IMPROVEMENTS ADD UP,

the problem of climate change, not less.

This is where the 80-plus percent figure comes in—an estimate by Boeing commonly cited in aviation circles. For the industry, it represents a huge untapped market and the hope that, as the pandemic abates, air traffic will resume its historical growth of about 5 percent a year. For so many of the more than 80 percent, affordable flights pose an opportunity for exploration and connection unthinkable not long ago. As someone who loves to fly and never tires of looking at landmarks below, clouds alongside, or stars above, I can't begrudge anyone the joy of flight.

At the same time, any journey in the skies warms the planet. Commercial aviation generally accounts for about 2.5 percent of all human-induced carbon dioxide emissions, but its true impact is far greater because of the warming effects of other pollutants and aircraft contrails, and the complex way these emissions linger and interact in the atmosphere. Some experts peg air travel as the source of up to 5 percent of the

France is moving toward a ban on all domestic air trips that can be made by train in less than two and a half hours. In the United Kingdom, the official Committee on Climate Change jolted the elite world of the most active fliers by proposing "a ban on air miles and frequent flyer loyalty schemes that incentivise excessive flying."

But trains versus planes is a straw man: Three-quarters of aviation fuel is used for trips of longer than 1,000 miles. At those distances, most people will opt to fly. Thunberg spent 15 days sailing across the Atlantic to make a point before she addressed the United Nations, but most people who need or want to travel across an ocean will do so by airplane—or not at all.

In that sense, flygskam is as much about the decision to travel as it is about the decision to fly. Aviation leaders contend that shaming flight is not the answer—greening it is.

"Aviation is an essential part of the global economy, so our challenge is reducing emissions and decarbonizing aviation, not preventing people who want to travel from traveling," says Sean

Newsum, the director of aviation sustainability strategy for Boeing. "That's really our foundational belief as an industry at this point."

AMONG THE POTENTIAL PATHS to green salvation for air travel, the quickest might be down a gravel road deep in the woods of central Georgia, leading to a hulking complex of pipes, pumps, tubes, tanks, and steel girders called the Freedom Pines Biorefinery. There I meet Curt Studebaker, a lanky, friendly young chemical engineer who is in the business of turning waste—all kinds of waste—into aviation fuel.

"The amazing thing is, once you get it right, it's really a better fuel even than Jet A," the standard kerosene fuel in U.S. aviation, Studebaker tells me. "It's actually cleaner."

Studebaker's employer, LanzaTech, could impress mad scientists anywhere: By capturing carbon-heavy emissions from a Chinese steel mill, mixing them with fast-chomping microbes originally discovered in the guts of a rabbit, adding water and nutrients, then allowing the mash

"scimitars" that now adorn the wingtips of many jets. But the most effective way to make them fly cleaner? Change the fuel.

With SAFs, carbon savings occur over their life cycle. Whether derived from agricultural by-products such as sugarcane stalks, or from industrial waste, or even municipal landfills, the SAF sequesters or consumes carbon early in the cycle, ultimately making it a much lower net emitter of carbon than fossil fuel.

And because it's a "drop-in" fuel, with relatively minor engine modifications needed, it wouldn't require new airport infrastructure, as alternatives to liquid fuel would.

The challenges? One, it's very expensive. Although more flights are using SAFs, it's a veritable drop in the bucket, well under 0.1 percent of the 95 billion gallons of fuel the industry used in 2019. This alternative fuel costs two to six times more than kerosene. Second, the industry can't rely on the easiest, cheapest sources for conversion: crops. If fuel producers were to gobble up land and water more urgently needed for food,

BUT NOT FAST ENOUGH TO CUT AVIATION'S
IMPACT ON CLIMATE CHANGE.

to ferment like a vat of beer, it created ethanol, which it refined at the Georgia plant.

The result: so-called sustainable aviation fuel, or SAF. Blended with Jet A, LanzaTech's invention powered a Virgin Atlantic Boeing 747 from Orlando, Florida, to London in 2018.

For now, SAFs, as just about everyone in the industry calls them, are still blended with standard fuel. But they are cast as the giant first step toward shrinking aviation's carbon footprint. The reason is simple: The tube-and-wing planes of today are expected by the airlines to last for two or possibly three decades. Their business plans depend on it. So even as engineers are thinking ahead to future generations of aircraft that may have radically different design features, or run on a different energy source, the thousands of planes already in the skies will be up there for a long time—and they will fly on liquid fuel.

Those jetliners will get somewhat more efficient as engines are replaced by newer models, or when mileage-improving enhancements are installed, such as the winglets, "sharklets," or

air travel would simply trade one environmental black eye for another.

So the industry has zeroed in on other promising sources, such as the waste LanzaTech converts to energy and halophytes, salt-tolerant plants that can be irrigated with seawater.

In a patch of desert along the Persian Gulf in the United Arab Emirates, oilseed plants known as *Salicornia bigelovii* feast on waste generated by fish and shrimp at an aquaculture farm. When ready for harvest, *Salicornia* seeds are separated and crushed to oil, then refined and mixed with kerosene to become alternative jet fuel.

Proponents contend that if SAF production were built to the scale needed to serve the bulk of aviation needs, the price would drop precipitously, becoming competitive with kerosene. But getting to scale is a classic chicken-or-egg dilemma. Unless there's demand, supply won't grow; but because the current supply is so small and costly, it's hard to stimulate demand. That's where the problem becomes political: The solution could be a carbon tax on kerosene or a

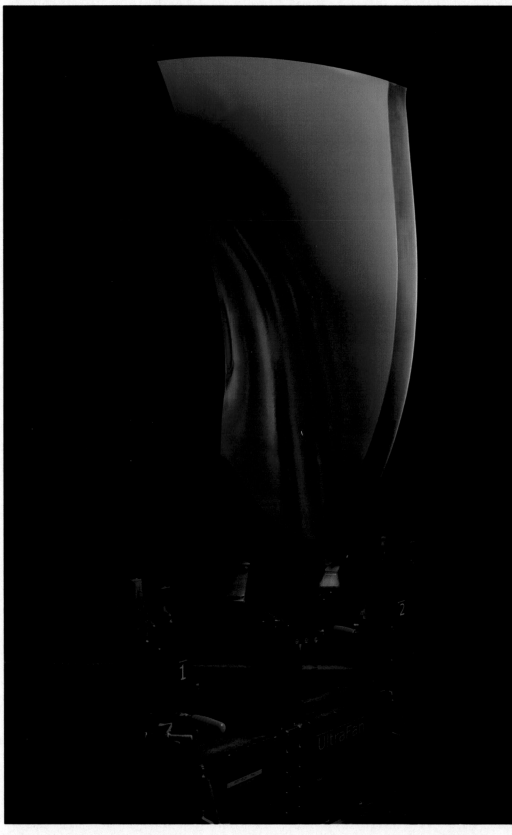

Innovative components in the Rolls-Royce UltraFan will help make the jet engine—slated to be the world's largest—lighter and more efficient. Each blade (left) will be made from a carbon fiber

composite; the compressor's rotor disk and blades (right) will be manufactured as an integrated unit.
The company aims to finish assembling its demonstration engine by the end of this year.

GREENER SKIES AHEAD

Today's jet fuel-powered planes will still serve many routes in the decades ahead. But engineers are hard at work designing the next generation of aircraft, from electric planes for short hops to revolutionary, hydrogen-powered models such as a prototype called Flying-V.

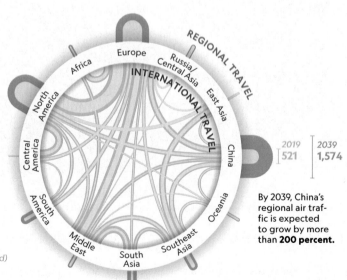

Cargo

Hydrogen tanks

Curbing a climb in emissions

By 2050, more than 10 billion passengers are expected to fly each year, double pre-pandemic travel numbers. If there were no improvements in technology, fuels, and operations, this would generate nearly two billion tons a year of carbon dioxide. The global industry has set a goal to cut that to 358 million tons—a third of today's emissions.

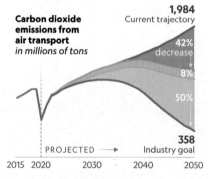

Carbon dioxide emissions from air transport
in millions of tons

1,984 Current trajectory

42% decrease

8%

50%

358 Industry goal

PROJECTED →

2015 2020 2030 2040 2050

Technology and Operations
Advances in materials such as carbon fiber can lead to lighter aircraft and lower emissions, as can low-tech advances including lighter weight paint and in-flight service carts. More efficient scheduling and route planning also can reduce the number of flights needed.

Sustainable Aviation Fuel
Airlines are now turning to fuels made from nonfossil sources such as algae (which absorb carbon from the atmosphere as they grow), helping to create a sustainable energy cycle.

Most growth will be in regional travel

Using sustainable fuels in commercial jets will help reduce emissions. That's good news because air travel is expected to expand globally—especially in Asia—as domestic economies grow.

Global air traffic demand
in billions of miles traveled by paying passengers

100 500 1,000

2019 2039 (projected)

International   Regional

REGIONAL TRAVEL

INTERNATIONAL TRAVEL

Africa · Europe · Russia/Central Asia · East Asia · North America · Central America · South America · Middle East · South Asia · Southeast Asia · Oceania · China

2019 **521** | 2039 **1,574**

By 2039, China's regional air traffic is expected to grow by more than **200 percent.**

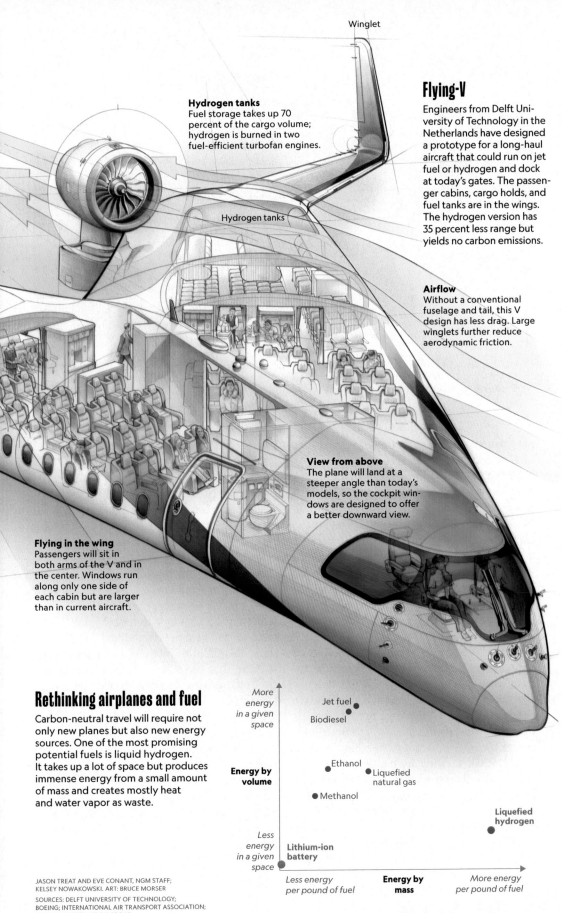

Winglet

Hydrogen tanks
Fuel storage takes up 70 percent of the cargo volume; hydrogen is burned in two fuel-efficient turbofan engines.

Hydrogen tanks

Flying-V
Engineers from Delft University of Technology in the Netherlands have designed a prototype for a long-haul aircraft that could run on jet fuel or hydrogen and dock at today's gates. The passenger cabins, cargo holds, and fuel tanks are in the wings. The hydrogen version has 35 percent less range but yields no carbon emissions.

Airflow
Without a conventional fuselage and tail, this V design has less drag. Large winglets further reduce aerodynamic friction.

View from above
The plane will land at a steeper angle than today's models, so the cockpit windows are designed to offer a better downward view.

Flying in the wing
Passengers will sit in both arms of the V and in the center. Windows run along only one side of each cabin but are larger than in current aircraft.

Rethinking airplanes and fuel

Carbon-neutral travel will require not only new planes but also new energy sources. One of the most promising potential fuels is liquid hydrogen. It takes up a lot of space but produces immense energy from a small amount of mass and creates mostly heat and water vapor as waste.

More energy in a given space

Jet fuel
Biodiesel

Energy by volume

Ethanol
Liquefied natural gas
Methanol

Liquefied hydrogen

Less energy in a given space

Lithium-ion battery

Less energy per pound of fuel

Energy by mass

More energy per pound of fuel

JASON TREAT AND EVE CONANT, NGM STAFF;
KELSEY NOWAKOWSKI. ART: BRUCE MORSER

SOURCES: DELFT UNIVERSITY OF TECHNOLOGY;
BOEING; INTERNATIONAL AIR TRANSPORT ASSOCIATION;
AIR TRANSPORT ACTION GROUP

Lilium has designed an electric jet engine (above) to power its small planes, while some other manufacturers are using dronelike electric propellers on theirs. The engines will be built into the wing flaps (right), which can be adjusted to provide vertical lift and horizontal thrust.

requirement that SAFs account for a percentage of all aviation fuel.

"Basically, there has to be a humongous ramp-up to SAFs," says Paul Stein, chief technology officer of Rolls-Royce, the British manufacturer whose next-generation UltraFan, the biggest and one of the most efficient jet engines ever, is designed to use the alternative fuel. "But industry is generally behind a SAF mandate. And certainly our position as a company is, yes! We need more SAFs. It would be a huge contribution to the planet."

AT AIRBUS HEADQUARTERS in the south of France there is a flying machine made of composite materials resembling no airliner that has ever taken to the skies, at least outside of science fiction movies or UFO sightings. In broad shape it resembles a bulbous manta ray. For a future passenger, a voyage in this *Star Trek*-like machine would be akin to flying in a movie theater.

No one will do so soon, though. The plane, known as Maveric, is a model aircraft with a 10.5-foot wingspan. For Airbus, the European consortium, Maveric's design could hold the answer to this intriguing question: Is there a more efficient—greener—way to design an airliner?

For all kinds of reasons, the modern aircraft manufacturing industry does not easily lend itself to the disruption that can so suddenly upend conventional thinking in other industries. A true game changer of an airliner will take many, many years to develop and more years to weather the gauntlet of safety tests involved in certification for commercial service.

Yet the so-called blended wing body design employed by Maveric—although with major technical challenges to overcome—could yield as much as a 40 percent reduction in carbon emissions compared with today's planes. The main advantage of the streamlined design is that the entire aircraft functions much like a wing, reducing drag and making it much easier to generate lift. In the Netherlands, researchers at Delft University of Technology used similar principles in designing Flying-V, an aircraft that looks very much like a boomerang.

Airbus created a major stir in the industry last year by announcing it was working on a line of aircraft with a 15-year timeline to service and a stunning capability: zero-emission flight. A Maveric variant and two smaller tube-and-wing airliners, it said, would operate on hydrogen fuel. The main by-product? Water vapor.

As is true with electric automobiles, zero emission doesn't necessarily mean zero pollution.

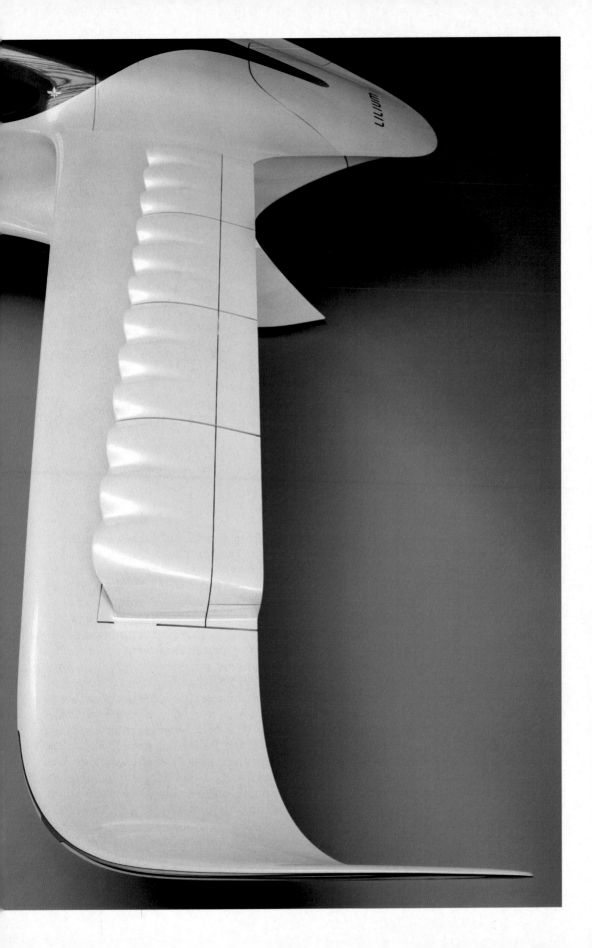

Just as it matters where the electricity comes from to charge the car's battery, Airbus's approach begs the question of how to create and store hydrogen fuel.

Most hydrogen used today comes from fossil fuels. But so-called green hydrogen, in which electricity is used to separate water into hydrogen and oxygen, is the holy grail. Advocates say that technological progress and scaling up will bring green hydrogen its day in the sky.

But there's another complication: Liquid hydrogen, such as that used in the U.S. space program, needs to be super-compressed and kept at cryogenic temperatures of minus 423°F to remain a liquid, which obviously requires significant energy. Conversely, in gaseous form, hydrogen would take up a huge amount of space in an airplane because the fuel tank would need to be much larger to yield the same amount of power as kerosene.

In either instance, a hydrogen-fueled airliner would be significantly different from today's planes, and airports would need new infrastructure to deal with it. Airbus acknowledges the hurdles but remains upbeat about the prospects.

"We strongly believe hydrogen is the necessary clean fuel to develop for aviation, because it's not just a question of reducing carbon dioxide emissions, it's about eliminating them altogether," says Amanda Simpson, vice president for research and technology at Airbus Americas. "If you get it from green hydrogen produced with electricity from sustainable sources—that's about as clean as you can possibly get!"

Boeing, which flew the world's first fully hydrogen-powered airplane in 2008, an experimental two-seater, is publicly less bullish. This is not because it questions hydrogen's potential but because the fuel is not the answer for many years to come.

"Our analysis is very clear that for commercial jets, sustainable aviation fuels are the only viable solution to really decarbonize over the near term or even the middle term," says Brian Yutko, Boeing's chief engineer for sustainability and future mobility. "We need to keep our eye on the ball and influence the outcomes there."

THE CENTRAL CALIFORNIA farm town of Hollister claims fame as the site of an annual motorcycle rally that inspired *The Wild One*, an early Marlon Brando hit. But these days it may be less notable for any roar in the streets than for a whisper-quiet device in the sky above the airport. Whirling around is a stubby, banana yellow aerial vehicle with 13 rotors—three on the front and back of each wing plus a larger pusher propeller in back. One more thing: There's no pilot.

The self-flying electric plane may be an oddity today, but its inventors expect it to be a commonplace of tomorrow—the aerial taxi. As more than one evangelist for the urban air mobility industry puts it, "Think: Uber meets Tesla in the sky."

Their company, called Wisk, is just one of many aspiring entrants, although with major chops: It has financial backing from Boeing and Kitty Hawk, the aviation start-up founded by Google's Larry Page. Its vision is a world in which taking a flying taxi will be as easy and affordable as an automobile ride is today—and safer to boot.

"This is not the Wild West," Gary Gysin, Wisk's chief executive, tells me when I visit the company's hangar. "We will absolutely meet the incredibly stringent safety standards already set for the aviation industry. We have to—nobody's flying anywhere until the FAA says so."

Airbus has test-flown a full-scale demonstrator of its CityAirbus, a multicopter powered by four square batteries (left). As seen from above, it has four propulsion units, each with two engines and two propellers (below). The aircraft is designed to fly autonomously at up to 75 miles an hour, ferrying four passengers on flights lasting no longer than 15 minutes. Airbus says it will be "ideal for aerial urban ride-sharing."

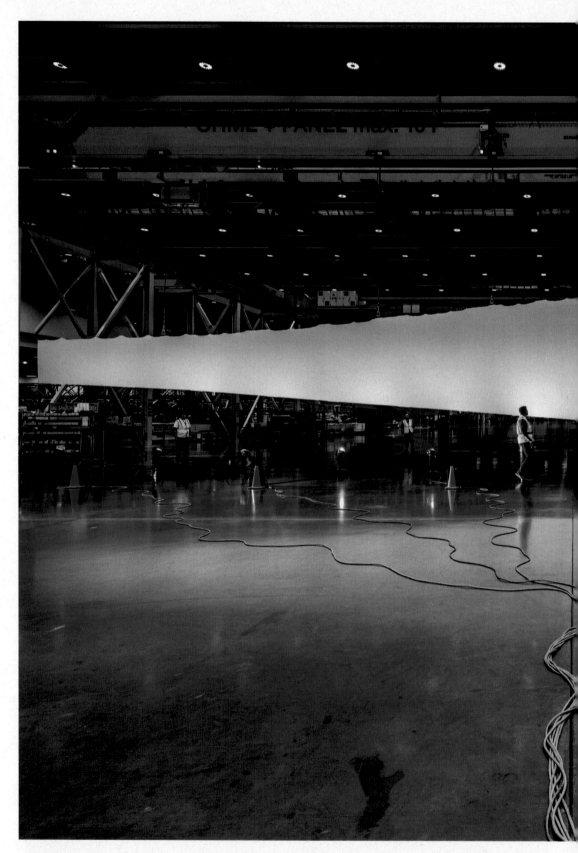

A 110-foot, upper-wing panel for Boeing's new 777X hangs from a gantry crane in its Everett, Washington, facility. The panel is made of layered carbon fiber tape, hardened by high heat and pressure. The 777X

has the biggest wingspan of any twin-engine jet—so long that each wing has a 12-foot tip that folds up, enabling the plane to fit at airport gates. Longer, lighter wings improve fuel efficiency.

Researchers at the Technical University of Munich are working with Airbus to study how algae might be used to create biofuels and make carbon fiber to construct lightweight airplanes. Algae absorb carbon dioxide from the atmosphere as they grow, so converting them to fuel creates a sustainable energy cycle.

Gysin is referring to the Federal Aviation Administration's regulatory process, but his broader contention is that remarkable advances in battery technology and lightweight composite materials, as well as the low operating costs of electric engines, make the vision feasible.

Just when this particular industry might take off is, well, up in the air. But it's serious business: Wisk's plane is one of more than 475 electric vertical takeoff and landing aircraft under development, according to the Vertical Flight Society.

Wisk's plane and other rival flying taxis can do what a helicopter does: pick people up and put them down in places fixed-wing aircraft can't. Aside from being much cheaper to operate, they are much, much quieter—a critical advantage given that helicopter services often have been stymied by noise complaints.

Gysin says the industry likely will start by shuttling people among airports and "vertiports," which might be a landing pad atop a Manhattan apartment building or a parking lot in a Los Angeles suburb. But as time goes on and people grow comfortable with safe, quiet, cheap air mobility?

"We'll be picking you up on your front lawn," Gysin says with a grin.

I joke that I might book a round-trip flight to nowhere just to admire the bird's-eye view.

"Absolutely!" Gysin shoots back with genuine enthusiasm. "The fun is part of the plan. That's a share of the market." In fact, he adds, he was a bit taken aback when initial marketing research disclosed that along with assurances of a safe, smooth, quiet ride, one feature most requested by potential customers was good Wi-Fi.

"And I'm like, Really? Are you kidding me?" he says, miming a smack to his head. "Put the dang phone away and look out the window!"

I'm some wild-eyed environmentalist hippie. I am a businessman. This is going to lower my costs, which is going to lower the cost of everyone's tickets."

Harbour Air is an ideal candidate for electric conversion: Its flights typically take less than 35 minutes, while the batteries can last at least an hour on a charge, offering ample reserve power.

Across the continent, Massachusetts-based Cape Air has embarked on a different milestone: It was the first airline in the world to announce plans to fly a brand-new, all-electric aircraft.

This plane, named Alice, is a streamlined, T-tailed, nine-passenger aircraft with twin propellers being built in Washington State by Eviation. The company's CEO, Omer Bar-Yohay, boldly if perhaps a tad hyperbolically predicts the plane will stake a claim to aviation fame right up there with the *Wright Flyer* and the Boeing 707.

"First we had powered flight, with propellers," he says. "Then we had the jet age. And now flight is entering the electric age."

Both Harbour Air's retrofit electric motors and Alice's new ones are built by magniX, a company in Everett, Washington. As with Harbour Air, Cape Air's routes, connecting Cape Cod with Boston and the nearby islands of Martha's Vineyard and Nantucket, are short hops. Dan Wolf, the airline's chief executive, says the electric power needed to charge Alice's batteries could come from Vineyard Wind, an offshore project under construction. That would make Cape Air's flights as clean as Harbour Air's.

Yet Alice is also an illustration of the challenges of electric flight: At 8,200 pounds, the batteries alone account for 60 percent of the plane's empty weight.

Electric-powered flight may hold out hope that flight can go green. Enthusiasts say that within 15 to 20 years, electric airliners could be carrying as many as 50 people a few hundred miles.

But for major air carriers flying much longer distances with lots more passengers, electric flight will be a chimera for many years to come. Someday, our descendants will take zero-emission flight for granted. But the problem of what we do between now and then remains a hugely vexing one, because that day isn't coming anytime soon. □

Just how strong a public backlash to the idea of air taxis there might be, I can't say. But electric-powered flight, while still severely limited by battery weight and capacity, is happening on another front. One intriguing approach is in British Columbia, Canada, where a commuter seaplane operator is retrofitting its workhorse fleet of 60-year-old de Havilland Beavers and Otters, swapping out gas-fired piston engines for electric motors.

Greg McDougall, Harbour Air's founder and chief executive, piloted the December 2019 initial test run on the first such plane. (The company's application for electric operation is making its way through the labyrinthine regulatory process.)

"We're proud to be the first airline in the world to offer completely clean electric flight, fueled by our province's sustainable hydropower," McDougall tells me. "But I'm not doing this just because

Sam Howe Verhovek is a Seattle-based writer and frequent contributor. **Davide Monteleone** is a photographer based in Zurich, Switzerland. This is his first feature for the magazine.

In the darkness

BY AMY MCKEEVER

A juvenile African
pompano, or threadfin
trevally, swims through
the Verde Island Pas-
sage, a major shipping
lane in the Philippines.
Its streaming filaments
resemble the tentacles
of a jellyfish—a possible
advantage for evading
predators that patrol
the night sea.

NIGHT LIFE

of the open water,

rarely seen creatures

dance along

the ocean current.

PHOTOGRAPHS BY

DAVID DOUBILET AND JENNIFER HAYES

☐ **The National Geographic Society,** committed to illuminating and protecting the wonder of our world, has funded Explorer David Doubilet since 2012. This is the 50th anniversary of his first assignment as a *National Geographic* photographer. Doubilet and Jennifer Hayes document both the beauty and the devastation in our oceans.

ILLUSTRATION BY JOE MCKENDRY

Hayes photographed a coin-size juvenile cowfish off Indonesia's coast. Doubilet likens this style of night diving—being carried by the currents—to drifting through space. "The only way to know which is up is to watch which direction the bubbles are going," he says.

Zooplankton—such as a jellyfish (left) and a larval lionfish surrounded by tiny, shrimplike amphipods (right)—often swim from the deep toward the surface at night to feed. Diving in the open ocean after sundown is "a grandstand seat to a parade of the most strange and exotic creatures in the world," Doubilet says.

The mirror image of a brilliantly colored flying fish is reflected on the underside of the sea's surface off Bermuda. Topside, these fish can glide up to 650 feet across the water by stretching out their pectoral fins like wings.

In the open ocean in the dead of night, a light-studded downline silently sinks a hundred feet into the water's inky depths.

Minutes later, there's a splash as divers plunge in too. Equipped with scuba gear, a bevy of lights, and waterproof DSLR cameras clipped to their suits, David Doubilet and Jennifer Hayes descend into a realm of the unimaginable.

"When you first get in, it is a galaxy of light," Doubilet says of black-water diving. "You see fellow divers with their shafts of focusing lights and red lights: a galaxy here and a galaxy there."

In the dark—whether it's the Sargasso Sea of the North Atlantic or the tropical waters off Indonesia's Raja Ampat archipelago—Doubilet and Hayes see things even many other marine biologists (Hayes is one) will never see. Black-water diving is "the equivalent of a marine 'Sorcerer's Apprentice,'" Doubilet says. "All strange things that are dancing around at night."

The duo capture rare images of creatures in their larval forms and observe the clever ways the animals survive the night, like a juvenile jack that hides behind a jellyfish. But as the current propels them through the sea, divers must keep an eye on their bubbles to remember which way is up—and on the downline's lights to make sure they don't drift too far from their boat.

"It's all at the mercy of the current," Hayes says. "You're just moving with [the animals], lucky to encounter them." □

A pelagic squid releases a cloud of ink before vanishing into the depths of Indonesian waters. The night sea can be mesmerizing, Doubilet says, but it can be frustrating to photograph because many animals are tiny and skittish: "As you move the focus, the creature spins this way or that, and you might not get it."

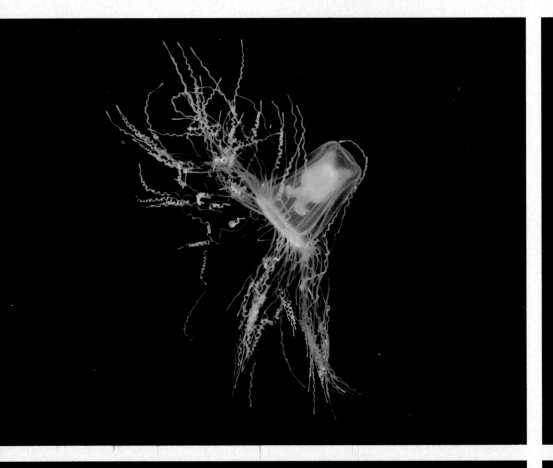

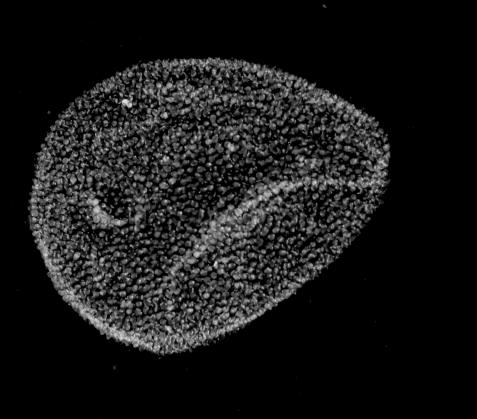

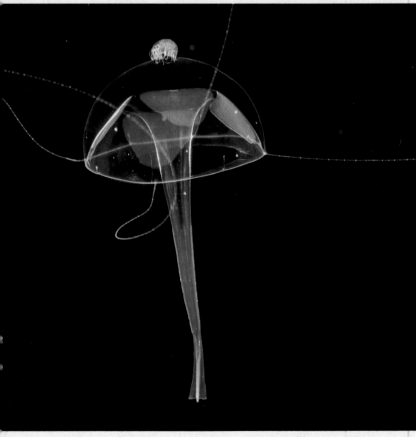

Black-water diving is "a never-ending story because your encounters are never the same," Hayes says. Clockwise from top left, a pinky fingernail-size immortal jellyfish can regenerate when injured; a larval carangid catches a ride on the bell of a moon jelly; an amphipod hitchhikes atop a jellyfish; and an unidentified egg mass drifts by.

To travel safely through the night sea, animals form unexpected alliances. This juvenile jack is hiding behind a jellyfish—and driving it like a motorboat. As the jellyfish provides protection from predators, the juvenile fish may feed on parasites that have latched onto its host. "You rarely run into something that doesn't fascinate you," Hayes says. "It really is a new macroscopic lens into the sea."

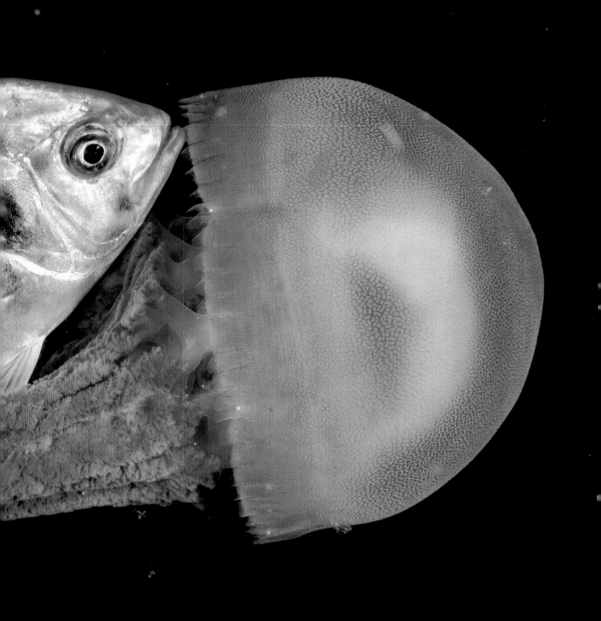

BY **MICHAEL FLETCHER**

PHOTOGRAPHS BY **ELIAS WILLIAMS**

A PLACE WHERE THE DREAM LIVES

THIS NEW YORK CITY COMMUNITY HAS A RICH TRADITION OF PROSPEROUS BLACK HOMEOWNERS. IN A NATION WITH A HISTORY OF RACIST HOUSING POLICIES, THAT'S RARE.

Black families began moving to the St. Albans area in Queens, New York, in the 1930s, despite restrictions that were designed to keep them from buying homes there. In 1948 the U.S. Supreme Court ruled that racial restrictions couldn't be enforced.

Eden Elder, in gray, splashes among friends and neighbors on an inflatable waterslide in the front yard where his father also played as a boy. The St. Albans home has been in the family for decades. Eden's grandmother, a retired principal, originally bought the house where they host this annual Independence Day party.

GROWING UP IN THE 1950S AND '60S, Olney Marie Ryland enjoyed visiting her aunt's house in Addisleigh Park, the most exclusive section of St. Albans, Queens. The neighborhood was only a mile from her family's home, but it exposed her to an entirely new world of high society, culture, and the arts.

"I used to think, That is where the rich people live," says Ryland, now 71.

Ryland's aunt lived in a wide-line Cape Cod with a before-its-time open-concept design, customized by her architect husband. Ryland's mother also had a friend who lived in the community, across the street from William "Count" Basie, the legendary jazz pianist and composer. Sometimes Ryland was invited to swim in Basie's pool.

In 1997, after her aunt turned frail and her home became available for purchase, Ryland and her husband jumped at the chance to buy it, swooping in just ahead of an investor. "The place has always been in my life," she says. "Thank God we were able to get it."

As it happened, the Rylands not only scored a beautiful home but also joined a rich tradition of Black homeownership that has thrived in and around St. Albans since the late 1930s—despite a series of racist policies aimed at keeping Black people out of the neighborhood.

They are obstacles that African Americans faced for generations when they tried to buy a home, a traditional gateway to prosperity for many Americans. Racial covenants once banned Black homeownership in St. Albans. After courts struck down those barriers, Black homeowners often faced harassment and even threats of violence from their white neighbors.

For decades, the federal government promoted racial segregation by redlining neighborhoods where Black people and other minorities lived, marking them as unacceptable

COMFORT IN RETIREMENT

Olney Marie Ryland, 71, created a miniature version (left) of her house in St. Albans. In 1997 Olney and her husband, Vernon Ryland, moved into the home after the death of her uncle, who designed it in the 1950s. Olney had a 30-year career managing pension plans, and Vernon spent 40 years with the U.S. Postal Service. Now retired with a pension, Olney spends her time singing in a choir and doing woodworking. "The place has always been in my life," she says. "Thank God we were able to get it."

A typical non-Hispanic white family's wealth is eight times that of a typical Black family—a legacy of bias in housing.

loan risks for government-backed mortgages and effectively starving them of capital needed to buy and improve homes. Black prospective homeowners were denied loans for houses in mostly white areas, charged higher fees for loans, or pushed to buy homes where mostly minorities lived. These practices depressed Black home-ownership, making it more expensive or more difficult for African Americans to buy houses.

By the time redlining was outlawed by the Fair Housing Act in 1968, white homeowners routinely were fleeing neighborhoods they felt were becoming too Black. More recently, banks and mortgage brokers targeted Black neighborhoods with subprime loans that had onerous fees and interest rates, contributing to a housing price bubble that spawned a foreclosure crisis once the bubble burst.

That long history of systemic racism has led to predictable results. Black people are far less likely than white people to own homes. And for Black homeowners, the experience often is more peril-ous: Houses in Black neighborhoods typically are worth less than those in white neighborhoods, making it harder for Black homeowners to build the kind of wealth that would allow them to pay for home improvements or weather job losses and other economic shocks.

"We can't circumvent the fact that [African Americans'] ability to buy homes was highly racialized from the start," says Anne Price, president of the Insight Center for Community Economic Development, which researches eco-nomic justice. "There was a very intentional exclusion of Black people from vehicles that allowed white people to buy homes and build equity from those homes. And that history is still very much a part of what we're seeing today."

At the end of 2019, the Black homeowner-ship rate was 42 percent, while 70 percent of white families lived in homes they owned. The 28 percentage point gap between Black and white homeowners was two points larger than the gap in 1960.

In the housing bust that triggered the 2008 recession, African Americans across the country lost nearly a quarter million homes. The housing crisis devastated Black families, causing the typ-ical household to lose more than half its wealth. No racial group escaped unscathed, but African Americans have suffered lasting damage from the downturn. Their rates of homeownership continued to decline for more than a decade. Preliminary data had hinted at a rebound in 2019—not long before the coronavirus pandemic delivered yet another economic blow.

The homeownership divide is a major contrib-utor to the nation's staggering racial wealth gap. Homes are the largest source of wealth accumu-lation for most Americans, and that's especially true for African Americans, who are less likely than white people to own other financial assets such as individual stocks or mutual funds.

The Federal Reserve Board's 2019 Survey of Consumer Finances found that a typical non-Hispanic white family in the U.S. had a net worth of $188,200, nearly eight times the wealth of a typical Black family.

The wealth gap between white and Black families is much larger than the income gap, and that difference "is entirely attributable to unconstitutional federal housing policy that was practiced in the mid-20th century," says Richard Rothstein, whose 2017 book, *The Color of Law*, details many of the ways that racially explicit policies and actions by all levels of government excluded Black people from much of the hous-ing market. "And the wealth gap locks African Americans even today into neighborhoods that are less well resourced than those whites live in."

Housing and Urban Development (HUD) sec-retary Marcia Fudge says the U.S. government is determined to enact policies to close the wealth gap. A big part of that, she says, is ensuring that high-quality homeownership opportunities are available to Black families at affordable interest rates. The Federal Housing Administration has updated its loan criteria to make it easier for prospective buyers with student loan debt to get federally insured mortgages. That should help Black buyers, who are disproportionately burdened with student debt.

"We're going to do everything we possibly can to make sure that every single person has an opportunity to build wealth for their families," Fudge said in late June. "We have never fully embraced the Fair Housing Act in this country; today, we're doing that."

THE LONG, DIFFICULT HISTORY endured by Black homeowners makes what's happened for the better part of a century in the St. Albans area all the more remarkable. "St. Albans tells America's fair housing story in microcosm," says Bryan Greene, a former HUD official who's now a vice president at the National Association of Realtors.

The first subdivisions in the community were on the drawing board by the turn of the 20th century, around the time that New York City's five boroughs were consolidated into a single city. Addisleigh Park was part of an early wave of development, says Greene, a St. Albans native. The enclave was modeled after English garden suburbs, with wide, tree-lined streets and sturdy colonial and Tudor homes set back on large, landscaped lots. A golf course was built in the neighborhood in 1915. It drew celebrities including legendary New York Yankees slugger Babe Ruth, who reportedly rented a home nearby.

Addisleigh Park was swank and, early on, exclusively white. A 1926 *New York Times* article about the sale of building lots said the neighborhood "carries a land and house restriction of the highest type." In the 1930s and '40s such indirect barriers were replaced by racial covenants with explicit rules: No Black people were allowed.

The restrictions eventually gave way, first informally, then legally. Pianist Thomas "Fats" Waller is credited with being among the first African Americans to buy a house in Addisleigh Park, moving there in 1938. Other Black homeowners soon followed. But in 1942, white residents sued a woman who was trying to sell her home to a Black man, saying the transaction would violate the agreement the prospective seller had signed banning sales to Black people. The restriction initially was upheld in court,

but it was struck down in 1948 when the U.S. Supreme Court ruled enforcement of restrictive covenants unconstitutional.

After that, more African Americans moved into the neighborhood. Through the years, Black luminaries including singer Lena Horne, baseball icon Jackie Robinson, civil rights activist W.E.B. Du Bois, heavyweight boxing champion Joe Louis, soul music superstar James Brown, and hip-hop pioneer LL Cool J have lived in St. Albans.

In the ensuing decades, the celebrities were joined by other upwardly mobile African Americans in southeast Queens. Bus drivers and plumbers, mail carriers and subway motormen, airport cargo handlers, corrections officers, teachers, principals, cops, and municipal clerks moved to the area, helping to transform it into one of the nation's largest and most vibrant centers of Black homeownership. But the change came with the type of struggle painfully familiar to Black homeowners across the country.

BARBARA EUBANKS moved to St. Albans with her family from Brooklyn in 1961. She remembers a beautiful, quiet neighborhood. But there were pockets of white hostility. Black-owned homes were sometimes pelted with eggs, and the new neighbors occasionally would be treated rudely by the old-timers.

"They would say things, call us names," recalls Eubanks, 73, a retired city traffic enforcement officer who still lives in St. Albans. "But basically we just ignored them."

Before long, she says, the white folks were gone anyway. "They moved, running—whether they could afford it or not." More Black families moved in, creating a modern enclave of Black middle-class life. The schools that would eventually educate her grandson, Elias Williams, who photographed this story, became more segregated.

Despite the challenges, southeast Queens was a powerful magnet for African Americans looking to buy a home with a little land around it.

In 1965, my parents pursued their version of the American dream when they bought a detached home in Springfield Gardens, not far from St. Albans. They'd owned a small row house in East Elmhurst, on the north side of Queens just across the bridge from our previous apartment in Harlem. We were a working-class family, and buying in southeast Queens was a step up.

At first, our block and the surrounding community were mostly *(Continued on page 114)*

Southeast Queens was a powerful magnet for African Americans looking to buy a home with a little land around it.

HEARTH AND HOME

Gregson and Bridgett Smith have lived in their St. Albans home for 24 years. Their children, Jaden and Justin (pictured above), played for two of the top baseball teams in Queens and became Eagle Scouts. Jaden, a junior at SUNY Cortland, studies psychology. Justin is heading to Howard University to study engineering.

Bridgett and Gregson first met in an airport when they were returning from separate vacations. Gregson is an electrical maintenance supervisor for NYC Transit, and Bridgett is a school social worker and owns a mental health consulting business.

THE OWNERSHIP GAP

In the United States, homeownership has long been heralded as a path to prosperity. The majority of homes with white residents have been owner-occupied since the 1950s, but for most Black Americans this gateway to success and stability has been blocked by racial discrimination, lower wages, and less access to credit. Recent census data show the white homeownership rate at 70 percent, compared with 42 percent for Black Americans—a gulf even larger than it was 100 years ago.

Black households by county, 2019
The size of a circle shows the number of housing units with a Black householder in each county.

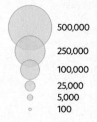

- 500,000
- 250,000
- 100,000
- 25,000
- 5,000
- 100

Black homeownership gap, 2019
Color shows the percentage point difference between white and Black homeownership rates.

PERCENTAGE POINTS

WIDER GAP →

- 56 (Double U.S. average)
- 42
- **28 (U.S. average homeownership gap)**
- 14
- 0
  - County where the Black homeownership rate is higher than the white homeownership rate

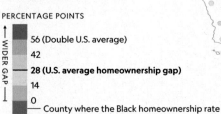

COUNTIES WITH FEWER THAN 100 BLACK HOUSEHOLDS ARE NOT SHOWN.
THE HOMEOWNERSHIP GAP IN ALASKA IS 31 PERCENTAGE POINTS. THE GAP IN HAWAII IS 32 PERCENTAGE POINTS.

A DISPARITY THROUGHOUT AMERICAN HISTORY

The end of slavery resulted in millions of Black Americans earning an income for their labor, sparking a steady increase in Black homeownership. Meanwhile, white homeownership rates dipped, as many moved from farms to rentals in cities. Federal incentives targeted at white people helped boost ownership after the Great Depression, and rates rose for all during the economic boom that followed World War II. Increases in Black homeownership in the 1950s and subsequent decades mirror hard-won gains in income and education during the civil rights movement.

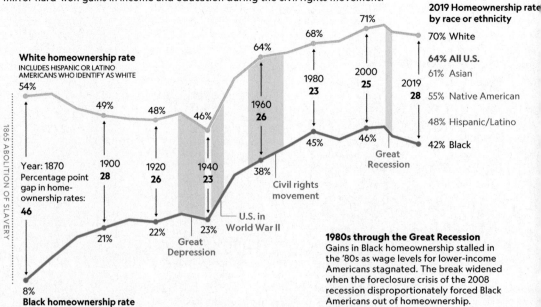

White homeownership rate
INCLUDES HISPANIC OR LATINO AMERICANS WHO IDENTIFY AS WHITE

54% · 49% · 48% · 46% · 1960 64% · 1980 68% · 2000 71% · 2019 70% White

1865 ABOLITION OF SLAVERY

Year: 1870 — Percentage point gap in home-ownership rates: **46**
1900 **28**
1920 **26**
1940 **23**
1960 **26**
1980 **23**
2000 **25**
2019 **28**

Great Depression
U.S. in World War II
Civil rights movement
Great Recession

8% — 21% — 22% — 23% — 38% — 45% — 46% — 42% Black
Black homeownership rate

2019 Homeownership rate by race or ethnicity
- 70% White
- **64% All U.S.**
- 61% Asian
- 55% Native American
- 48% Hispanic/Latino
- 42% Black

1980s through the Great Recession
Gains in Black homeownership stalled in the '80s as wage levels for lower-income Americans stagnated. The break widened when the foreclosure crisis of the 2008 recession disproportionately forced Black Americans out of homeownership.

RILEY D. CHAMPINE, NGM STAFF; SCOTT ELDER. SOURCES: WILLIAM J. COLLINS, VANDERBILT UNIVERSITY, AND ROBERT A. MARGO, BOSTON UNIVERSITY, "RACE AND HOME OWNERSHIP FROM THE END OF THE CIVIL WAR TO THE PRESENT," *AMERICAN ECONOMIC REVIEW*, 2011; ELLORA DERENONCOURT, PRINCETON UNIVERSITY; IPUMS NATIONAL HISTORICAL GEOGRAPHIC INFORMATION SYSTEM, UNIVERSITY OF MINNESOTA; U.S. CENSUS

The greatest divide
In the Minneapolis metro area the white homeownership rate is 76 percent while the Black homeownership rate is 26 percent—the widest gap among large U.S. cities.

Northern barriers to entry
When Black Americans left the South in great numbers during the 20th century, many arrived in urban areas where racist backlash to those migrations would limit housing options.

A more equitable South
For decades Black homeownership rates have been relatively high in the South, where rural Black households are common. Suburbs of some southern cities are seeing a return of Black families from the North.

New York City boroughs
(county-equivalent name)

Queens

Brooklyn
(Kings)

Bronx

Manhattan
(New York)

Staten Island
(Richmond)

FINDING PARITY

At the county level, places where the Black homeownership rate is the same as or higher than the white homeownership rate are few and far between (map above). Queens, with its long-standing Black middle-class neighborhoods like St. Albans, is by far the largest example of a county with homeownership equity.

— **Black households**
Each circle represents 100 households

Homeownership rate, 2019

Queens, N.Y.   White ●● Black
                46%   48%

New York City
metropolitan
area   32%   61%

United States   42%   70%

BERGEN CO.
26
|
Percentage
point gap in
homeownership
rate by county

WESTCHESTER CO.
36

Mt. Vernon

PASSAIC CO.
36

ESSEX CO.
34

Newark

HUDSON CO.
10

Jersey City

Bronx
10

— Harlem

Manhattan
20

Queens
-2

NASSAU CO.
16

LONG ISLAND

Addisleigh Park

St. Albans

UNION CO.
24

Brooklyn
8

Staten Island
40

5 mi
5 km

STAR POWER IN ST. ALBANS

CLOCKWISE FROM TOP LEFT

This Linden Boulevard house is the former home of singer James Brown, one of many Black celebrities who resided in Addisleigh Park, a historic section of St. Albans, Queens.

In this Murdock Avenue house on Christmas Day, 1955, heavyweight boxing champion Joe Louis married Rose Morgan, a prominent beauty parlor magnate and style influencer.

Beloved singer Ella Fitzgerald, who got her big break at Harlem's Apollo Theater and rose to international acclaim, lived in this Murdock Avenue home in the 1950s.

William "Count" Basie, the legendary jazz pianist and composer, lived in this Adelaide Road house. He was one of the first celebrities to move to St. Albans in the 1940s, influencing other well-known Black entertainers and athletes who made the neighborhood home.

BEHIND THE STORY

A PASSION INSPIRED BY FOND MEMORIES

Photographer Elias Williams spent the first 15 years of his life in and around St. Albans, the Queens enclave that would become the primary subject of his photographic pursuits.

Williams, his mother, and his sister lived with his grandmother, Barbara Eubanks, on a leafy block with friendly neighbors. Later he would learn about the grand history of St. Albans, the many celebrities who lived there, and its role as a pillar of New York City's Black middle class.

"The community's uniqueness in terms of its history was just regular to me," Williams says. "I've always known one house, having a front yard and backyard, and it was always quiet. You spoke to everybody, everybody spoke to you."

When he was a freshman in high school, the idyll of his early childhood was stripped away. With his mom and sister, Williams moved to a nearby apartment complex, but that arrangement was short-lived. The family fell into homelessness, forcing Williams to move in with his godmother for a few weeks before joining his mother and sister at a shelter in the Bronx. Living in shelters meant curfews, more than a two-hour subway and bus commute to high school, and no friends coming over because no visitors were allowed.

"We lived two to three years in shelters before we finally got our first apartment in the Bronx," he says. Since then, he has moved several times, but St. Albans remains close to his heart.

Williams, 30, was introduced to photography in high school, and he decided to pursue it as a profession when he was a student at LaGuardia Community College in Queens.

His focus on his old neighborhood, where his grandmother still lives, was motivated by a class assignment to document the lives of residents elsewhere in Queens, as well as by the work of two friends who frequently made dignified portraits of people of color.

"That really became my earliest inspiration for me wanting to focus on my own community," he says. "Because they were focusing on theirs, I thought I should focus on mine."

His work in St. Albans began in 2012, and it continues as he adds new themes. "The layers of the housing crisis and using the work as a form of reflection because of how I eventually lived in a shelter would come later," he says. "So the project has gone through many, many stages of how I wanted to display it, and the conversation I wanted to have surrounding the work. At its core, though, it's really about highlighting the everyday people in this community and putting them on the same plane as the legends and celebrities."

Williams eventually wants to publish the project as a book and display it in a photo exhibition.

Although Williams still lives in the Bronx and keeps up with his work from there, he says he will always call St. Albans home.

"I have a lot of love for the Bronx," he says, "but I'll always be a Queens kid." —MF

white. That changed quickly. Within two or three years, nearly all the white families had moved, leaving the neighborhood overwhelmingly Black with young families in almost every home. That suited me just fine. Our summers were filled with street games from skelly to box ball and tag games from ring-a-levio to manhunt. We played dodgeball at day camp, touch football in the street, basketball, stickball, and handball at the playground, and we went on long bike rides. We avoided areas where you might be attacked for being Black, but that was easy because you could go several miles in most directions and still be in a Black neighborhood.

It wasn't until many years later that I realized that our homes were not worth as much as almost identical houses in nearby white communities. It wasn't just my old neighborhood. A 2018 study led by Brookings Institution researcher Andre Perry found that "homes of similar quality in neighborhoods with similar amenities are worth 23 percent less ($48,000 per home on average, amounting

to $156 billion in cumulative losses) in majority Black neighborhoods, compared to those with very few or no Black residents." The report made clear that there's a tax on Black homeowners that has continued, in one form or another.

GROWING UP IN AN APARTMENT in the South Jamaica Houses, a low-income development known locally as the 40 Projects, Loree Sebastien knew a different world was just two miles away in St. Albans. It was a world of sturdy homes and manicured lawns, owned by Black folks.

Sebastien's mother would drive her and her sister through the neighborhood, pointing out homes where Black celebrities once lived. Those drives planted a seed in her mind that blossomed once she became an adult and bought a three-bedroom colonial in St. Albans two decades ago. "I just grew up hearing that there is a rich legacy here, that you might not find a cluster of Black homeowners like this anywhere in the country," says Sebastien, 48, a computer

programmer. "When I moved here, I knew I was moving up."

She wasn't disappointed when she moved in. The streets were immaculate, the neighbors friendly. "It is a prosperous, supportive place that is more quiet, nicer, neater than I thought."

Sebastien busied herself updating her home. She decorated each room in a different ethnic theme. She has a Japanese bedroom and Chinese and Mexican bathrooms. But soon enough, she learned things were not as idyllic as they appeared. When the foreclosure crisis hit several years after she bought her home, Sebastien was stunned by how many people in the neighborhood were hurt by the fallout.

"I am upper middle class, and to have to go through this was amazingly shocking," she says. "It was like being in the projects again, watching neighbors being evicted. It decimated the area."

At one point, her own mortgage servicer mistakenly began moving her property toward foreclosure. She hired a lawyer who quickly found the

Paintings, fine china, and framed photographs decorate the rooms of Eubanks's home. "I like it neat, kept up, and presentable where the neighborhood doesn't look bad and my house doesn't look tacky," she says. "Other than that, it's just a home. You live in it and enjoy it." Eubanks moved with her family to St. Albans from Brooklyn in 1961. Her homes have been gathering places for family and for the community. She has hosted commercial art shows in her living room, and the fold-out bed in this well-cared-for, 35-year-old couch has allowed her to welcome family members for holidays and other visits.

Despite the turmoil of the housing crisis more than a decade ago, St. Albans remains a vibrant community with many longtime residents.

A PLACE TO CELEBRATE

The Isaacs, Jewel Linda and Edward, purchased their Camden Avenue house in 1980. Jewel is a retired library manager, and Edward is a regional vice president at Primerica financial services after a 29-year career at Dow Jones and a decade as a professor at Medgar Evers College. Training from the U.S. Air Force helped Edward get well-paid technical work early on. The Isaacs are leaders of the Camden Avenue Block Association, one of the oldest block groups in St. Albans, and often hosted holiday parties in their home. Edward is president, Jewel is recording secretary.

The Isaacs' refrigerator is covered with photos of friends and family collected during the 41 years they have lived in St. Albans.

problem: a paperwork error made when her mortgage changed hands among several companies after she bought her home. "If you didn't have my background and the money to hire a lawyer, who knows what would have happened?" she says.

Many of Sebastien's neighbors suffered much crueler fates, as did many Black homeowners across the country. Southeast Queens was the area of New York City hardest hit by the foreclosure crisis, which was directly linked to the high number of subprime home loans made in the years before the housing bubble burst.

In 2006, 60 percent of all new home loans in the greater St. Albans area were high-cost loans, compared with 23 percent citywide, according to New York University's Furman Center for Real Estate and Urban Policy. Many homeowners had been lured into expensive subprime loans with high interest rates even though they could have qualified for less expensive mortgages.

"With predatory mortgages, we are always grinding to keep up," says I. Daneek Miller, a New York City council member representing southeast Queens. Miller, a former bus driver and union leader, says he has tried to help many families in mortgage distress. Despite a patchwork of government programs aimed at helping people avert foreclosure, he says, too often people showed up so late in the process that they were beyond help.

"Early on, I think people are embarrassed," he says. "Then they don't reach out until the marshal is at the door."

The situation in southeast Queens was repeated nationally. From 2007 to 2015, homes in Black communities were twice as likely to tumble into foreclosure as those in white communities, according to the real estate firm Zillow.

Through it all, Miller says, southeast Queens has remained a center of Black homeownership. New affordable condominiums are now luring young buyers, and many people raised in family-owned homes there have continued the tradition.

"This is the enclave of homeownership in the city," Miller says. "We have such a rich, rich legacy, and we have to keep it up."

KEITH BROWN AND GERI TAYLOR-BROWN grew up in St. Albans, beginning in the mid-1950s. Early in their marriage, they lived in a nearby 20-building housing cooperative called Rochdale Village. But they wanted a home with a yard, and they looked to buy in their old neighborhood.

"Both of us were raised in houses, and we wanted to return to that," says Geri, 68, a retired school superintendent.

Many of their friends moved to towns in Nassau County, but the Browns wanted to uphold the tradition they grew up in.

"At the time, I had a real strong belief that when Black neighborhoods went down, it was because we abandoned them rather than staying and making it a better place," says Keith, 71, a retired bus driver who for more than 50 years has coached and helped manage high school and youth football teams.

They got a taste of the challenges Black homeowners face after buying their three-bedroom

Homeowners Keith Brown (second from left in back row) and Geri Taylor-Brown (in blue dress on couch at far right) sit for a family portrait after an Easter dinner. Now both retired, Keith spends time as a football coach, and Geri served on the community board until June.

colonial in 1988. The boiler went out, and they had little cash, having poured it all into their new home. They applied for a loan to cover the $3,000 repair bill but were turned down by one lender after another. Eventually they borrowed the money from Keith's parents. "We later learned that Black homeowners were being rejected for loans based on their zip code," Geri says.

The couple raised their three children in St. Albans, and now the children, their spouses, and 11 grandchildren are regular visitors.

The Browns have seen residents and businesses come and go. They've watched an influx of neighbors from the Caribbean and South Asia. They were alarmed by all the homes that turned over because of foreclosures, and by investors who crowded two-family houses onto small lots.

This year they put their home up for sale, saying that as they age, their stairs are becoming difficult to navigate. But St. Albans will always be home.

"People can't start talking to us about where we live without us starting to brag," Geri says. "I let them know I was born in Harlem Hospital and I live in St. Albans. So don't mess with me." ☐

Michael Fletcher, a senior writer with ESPN, spent his formative years in southeast Queens. **Elias Williams** is a New York-based photographer whose work honors the cultural and historical significance of those in underrepresented communities.

Saving chimps, and finding hope amid chaos

At a Central African sanctuary,
traumatized chimpanzees are models
of resilience for their rescuers.

BY PAUL STEYN   PHOTOGRAPHS BY BRENT STIRTON

Anthony Caere, a pilot for Virunga National Park in the Democratic Republic of the Congo, cradles Felix and Mara as he flies them to Lwiro Primates Rehabilitation Center. The babies' families were killed by poachers. Caere, who survived a plane crash in 2017, says helping to rescue chimps gives him purpose.

Itsaso Vélez del Burgo
(at left), the technical
director of the sanctu-
ary, plays with baby
chimp Mara while Oziba
Miderho Mireille,
one of Lwiro's caregivers,
has Felix in her lap.
Orphaned chimps are
lonely and often trau-
matized. When they
arrive at Lwiro, they're
assigned caretakers
who give them love
and attention to help
them heal.

AFRICA

Lwiro Primates Rehabilitation Center

DEMOCRATIC REPUBLIC OF THE CONGO

Itsaso Vélez del Burgo held the wild baby chimp in her arms. Limp and unconscious, the female ape wasn't much bigger than a human hand.

Her tiny body and lack of teeth revealed that she was only about a month old. She was battling hypothermia and dehydration, and if something wasn't done in a hurry, her heart would stop.

"She was the youngest chimp we had ever taken in," says Vélez del Burgo, the technical director of Lwiro Primates Rehabilitation Center, a refuge in the eastern part of the Democratic Republic of the Congo (DRC). It was June 16, 2017, and Vélez del Burgo had facilitated a grueling, five-day rescue journey via motorcycle, speedboat, and car to get the baby chimpanzee safely to the village of Lwiro. A contact from an anti-poaching group had found the chimp with several poachers in the dense rainforest near the remote town of Pinga, about 180 miles away. After handing over the baby, the men revealed that her twin sister had died shortly after they shot her mother.

The National Geographic Society, committed to illuminating and protecting the wonder of our world, has funded Explorer Brent Stirton's journalism about humans and the environment since 2017.

ILLUSTRATION BY JOE MCKENDRY

At the sanctuary, the battle for the chimp's life was just beginning. Vélez del Burgo quickly covered the inert body with warm blankets and administered intravenous fluids. At last, the baby stirred and her eyes opened.

"I let her sleep in my breast to keep her warm," says Zawadi Balanda, a quiet, young Congolese assigned to watch Busakara, as they'd named her that night. Vélez del Burgo was worried that with no natural mother to feed her and provide emotional support, the baby chimp would fade away.

CHIMPANZEES, along with bonobos, are our closest living relatives. Their numbers throughout Africa are estimated at no more than 300,000—down from perhaps a million at the start of the

Orphaned chimps learn how to live in Lwiro's forested enclosure. They establish a pecking order, forage, play, and gaze at what lies beyond the fence. Lwiro aims to release as many chimps as possible back into the wild.

20th century—because of poaching for bushmeat, smuggling for the pet trade, and habitat loss.

Lwiro Primates Rehabilitation Center was founded in 2002 when war in the DRC spurred bushmeat poaching in nearby Kahuzi-Biega National Park. Wildlife authorities confiscated orphaned chimps from poachers and villagers, housing them in old lab rooms at an abandoned Belgian science research center in Lwiro. As the numbers of orphans grew, two institutions—the

Every afternoon care-givers feed the chimps a nourishing mix of corn, soy, sorghum, flour, and protein. The chimps also are given a daily menu of vegetables, fruit, and beans from local markets. This demand for food accounts for about $4,000 a month in much needed revenue for farmers in the area.

Congolese Institute for the Conservation of Nature and the National Center for Research in Natural Sciences, also based in the DRC—created the sanctuary. Bernard Masunga, a senior veterinarian who's been at Lwiro since its inception, has seen the haven grow into a home to chimps and monkeys, more than a hundred each, in forested enclosures. "I am very proud of local efforts to arrive where we have arrived," he says. But as primates keep coming, he says, the long-term strategy is to release as many as possible back into the wilderness once they've regained health and confidence.

Sitting with a group of chimps one day last year, Vélez del Burgo flips her phone's camera to selfie mode and points at the curious apes. Billi, a six-year-old male, looks with what seems to be amusement at the image on the screen. A few other chimps peer over his shoulder. Billi bares his lips to examine and pick his teeth. Then he squishes his cheeks with his fingers as if popping pimples. Vélez del Burgo chuckles as Billi pokes a forefinger up his nose.

"I'D ALWAYS DREAMED of working in primate conservation," says the soft-spoken Vélez del Burgo, who arrived at Lwiro in early 2014, when the sanctuary had about 55 chimps. Born in Vitoria, a small town in northern Spain, she felt a call to protect animals.

"Even at school, I would find troubled insects and keep them from harm," she says. Her mother, an immigrant from Colombia with very little money, helped her through university in Barcelona, where she received a master's degree in primatology. Vélez del Burgo's interest in primate behavior drew her to Guinea, in West Africa, to research chimps in the wild.

When a volunteer position came up at Lwiro, she seized the opportunity to get even closer to wild chimps. But nothing had prepared her for the challenges of living in a region torn by previous wars and still undergoing conflict. In her third month, "Mai-Mai rebels came in from the forest to attack the military," she says. Some nights, Vélez del Burgo would lie in bed shaking as the din of bombs, grenades, and machine-gun fire made sleep impossible.

Then Lwiro's director was stricken by a mysterious illness, nearly died, and had to be air-lifted out of the area. "It was a stressful time," says Vélez del Burgo, who became the sanctuary's manager, responsible not only for caring for numerous orphaned primates but also for fundraising, maintaining the facilities, and managing the sanctuary's then 31 staff members.

When little Busakara arrived in a bundle of rags in mid-2017, the sanctuary held some 75 chimps, and the numbers were growing each month. Vélez del Burgo saw something special about Busakara that gave her strength during a time when the extreme isolation and constant security threats weighed heavily. Busakara was completely helpless, Vélez del Burgo says, but "I was surprised by her resilience. She really wanted to live."

AFTER BUSAKARA SURVIVED her first precarious night, a team of caregivers—surrogate mothers—was assigned to provide the round-the-clock support the baby would have had from her own mother. Balanda was one of the surrogates. She grew up on a subsistence farm and says she never dreamed that one day she'd be looking after orphaned chimps. Throughout her teens

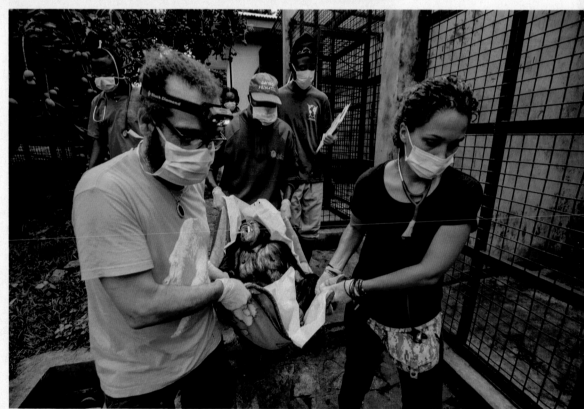

Vélez del Burgo plays with Mara, Felix, and Mubaki (left to right). Mubaki, which means "survivor" in Swahili, was close to death when he arrived at the sanctuary. He'd been mistreated by poachers who killed his mother and planned to sell him into the pet trade. To help them recover, young chimps need to play with one another as their distinctive personalities emerge.

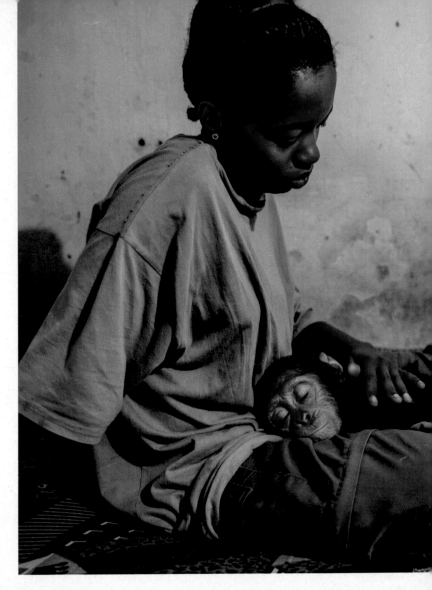

Caregiver Mireille sits with Mara and Felix as they sleep. Infant chimps, like human babies, require round-the-clock care. If a baby chimp wakes up frightened in the middle of the night, the surrogate mother must be on hand to lull the little one back to sleep.

and into adulthood, she endured repeated brutal assaults by rebel soldiers that eventually landed her in the hospital, where she underwent reconstructive surgery. That's when she met someone from Lwiro and was offered the chance to join the sanctuary as a caregiver.

"She arrived at Lwiro destroyed," Vélez del Burgo says. "She would not talk, would not socialize with humans." Helping staff with their own traumatic experiences is a part of her job that Vélez del Burgo hadn't expected. "In Congo there is so much suffering from both animals and humans," she says. "I am a very sensitive person, so I kind of close myself to the human suffering. I do not think I can deal with everything."

At first, Balanda was afraid of the chimps,

but gradually she learned their subtle communications, how to groom them, how they laugh hysterically when you tickle them—the *oh oh oh* that's eerily similar to our laughter—and vocalizations that mean yes and no.

Balanda says the chimp named Busakara had diarrhea in her first days at the sanctuary. "I was cleaning her and sleeping with her to keep her warm," Balanda says with a fond smile. "She would sometimes cry when I left in the morning." Human love and attention were vital in the early months of Busakara's healing, but even more meaningful rehabilitation began when she was well enough to join half a dozen other young chimps in a raucous, rough-and-tumble nursery and develop her own personality.

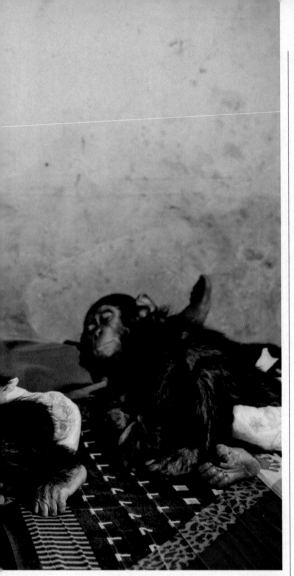

recovering chimps, free to develop a natural hierarchy and family unit. Busakara soon built good relationships with the other chimps. "She became very nurturing," Vélez del Burgo says. "We put new, very traumatized chimps with her because she was the welcoming one."

In 2019 there was a surge in arrivals of new chimps—a record nine. Virunga National Park, a partner of Lwiro's, had donated flight costs and a pilot to assist with aerial transfers of orphans recovered in remote regions in the DRC. Then in December, a bad bout of flu hit the sanctuary. More than 90 percent of the chimps contracted the virus, and two died. Busakara became very ill, but Lwiro's veterinarians managed to help her pull through.

In March 2020, when the novel coronavirus took hold in the DRC, Vélez del Burgo was fraught with worry about the chimps, the monkeys, and the staff. "Chimpanzees are highly susceptible to respiratory diseases," she says. "We did not know the effect the coronavirus could have."

There were reports of numerous orphaned chimps in various parts of the country, but under lockdown, no one could get them to the sanctuary. The uncertainty, coupled with a plunge in donor funding, increased the pressure. But a lifeline came in the form of support from the Ivan Carter Wildlife Conservation Alliance, a partner conservation organization that spearheaded a funding drive to keep the sanctuary going. "There were some days," says Vélez del Burgo, "when I thought, I cannot do this anymore."

There were many rewarding days too, often spent in the presence of Busakara, inspiring Vélez del Burgo to persevere. "Busakara is one of the few chimps who will walk up to me on her hind legs," she says, laughing. "She came to us so young, she learned to walk like a human."

Vélez del Burgo has come to understand how important Lwiro is to members of the staff, such as Balanda, who in helping chimps recover find that the animals help them in return. That goes for Vélez del Burgo herself. The biggest lesson the chimps have taught her, she says, is how to be strong in the face of struggle. "They never give up." Life here is not easy, she says, "but I won't abandon them—the chimps or the team." □

Balanda's confidence also was growing, and she began looking after the older orphans too. Her new relationship with the chimps was helping her emerge from a dark depression. "Little by little, you could see her smiling and talking to me more," Vélez del Burgo says. "She was finally able to tell you more about the experience she had."

Balanda's newfound passion for the chimps inspired her to enroll in a veterinary science course at the university in Lwiro. "I always thought I would be a vet with farm animals," Balanda says. "I never thought I would be working with wild chimps!"

After two years, Busakara was released into one of Lwiro's natural forested enclosures. She would learn to live with a proxy family of

Paul Steyn is a filmmaker and journalist from South Africa who contributes stories to *National Geographic* about African conservation. Award-winning photojournalist **Brent Stirton** is a frequent contributor to the magazine.

INSTAGRAM

ENRIC SALA

FROM OUR PHOTOGRAPHERS

WHO

Sala is a marine ecologist and National Geographic Explorer in Residence.

WHERE

San Ambrosio Island in the Pacific Ocean, some 550 miles west of Chile

WHAT

A Nikon D800 with a 10.5mm fish-eye lens

In 2008 Sala launched the Pristine Seas project, which has helped scientists study sensitive marine habitats—and inspired the protection of more than 2.3 million square miles of ocean. He captured this moment in 2013, as cinematographer Manu San Félix emerged from a kelp forest with a baby lobster on his mask (it soon scurried off). The expedition resulted in the creation of Nazca-Desventuradas Marine Park, one of the largest such sanctuaries in the Americas. Visit *nationalgeographic.org/projects/pristine-seas*.

This page showcases images from the Instagram accounts of National Geographic—the most popular brand on Instagram. Join more than 245 million followers: **@natgeo, @natgeotravel, @natgeointhefield, @natgeoadventure, @natgeoyourshot.**